Opus IV

Opus IV

Napa Valley Writers
2023 Anthology

Prose and poetry from members
of the Napa Valley Writers
A Branch of the California Writers Club

ISBN: 978-0-9985108-2-8

Print Edition November 2023

Cover and Interior Design: Jo-Anne Rosen

Published by: Gnarly Vine Press
Address: P.O. Box 5901
Napa, CA 94581

Our *Opus IV* Anthology is dedicated

to all those who support writers.

~

"I wish you could see that I write in blue ink

the color of oceans and early mornings"

— Jalynn Harris

Napa Valley Writers Anthologies

2017 First Press
2019 Meritage
2021 Third Harvest
2023 Opus IV

Foreword

Welcome to *Opus IV*, our 2023 Napa Valley Writers Anthology. This, our fourth biannual Anthology (2017, 2019, 2021, 2023), presents the writing of approximately half of our members. As in previous editions, we feature collected literary works in poetry, fiction, and creative nonfiction that have been reviewed, selected, and curated by our team of editors. The work in *Opus IV* ranges from short poems to longer stories, memoirs and essays reflecting the diverse talent and experience of our writers. Some of our authors are published here for the first time and some are published for their hundredth. We congratulate all of them for this appearance in print—a common and lofty goal for many writers.

The mission of Napa Valley Writers is to support and promote our members and the literary arts in our community and beyond. *Opus IV* is a major part of that effort, and we are proud to offer these creative expressions from the hearts and minds of writers who share their experience. Here, we trust, you will find writing that will touch and amuse you, provide new insight, expand your horizon, make you laugh, offer you solace and more. All this from simple strokes and shapes on a page making human connections through imaginative language.

— John Petraglia, Managing Editor

Genre Introductions

"The daily routine of most adults is so heavy and artificial that we are closed off to much of the world . . . I think one purpose of art is to get us out of those routines. When we hear music or poetry or stories, the world opens up again." Ursula K. Le Guin, as quoted by Jonathan White in *Talking on the Water*, 2016.

The poetry presented here in three sections invokes love and relationships, the beauties of nature, and varied life experiences. As you explore the fine poetry by our writers, consider how emotions and observations are expressed in thoughts and through chosen words.

With careful eyes and dedication, my peers and I pored over the poems submitted this year by 24 Napa Valley writers. I offer deep gratitude to my team of reviewers: Lance Burris, Edgar Calvelo, and 2021–2023 Napa County Poet Laureate Marianne Lyon. I make special note of their assiduous and devoted attention to each poem in this collection.

In addition, I thank Deanna M. Griffin for her capable and frequent technical support. Finally, sincere thanks to John Petraglia, Managing Editor of Opus IV, for his leadership and guidance. You are invited to approach the three sets of poems in this anthology as a break from your daily routine. May you find poetry here that resonates for you and opens your world.

— Poetry Editor, Antonia Allegra

Our fiction selection contains a variety of genres and styles, including sci fi, magical realism, and drama from the grave. Many of these stories are about family: parents' efforts to provide for and connect with their children or to have a fun vacation while exploring history, and a husband's work to protect loved ones from an oncoming storm. We also see the longing that comes with love, alongside the troubles that often follow. These stories offer lyrical connections to nature, reminiscences of special times lost but not forgotten, and concern for the political forces that threaten the future.

It has been an easy pleasure to work with this team of editors: Brien Crothers, Geoffrey K. Leigh, Marty Malin, Aletheia Morden, and Gary Orton. The passion the authors have instilled in their prose and the editors' skill and positive attitudes in helping to refine the work make for a fine collection of stories. There is something here for everyone and I hope you will find entertainment and inspiration in these pages.

— Fiction Editor, Lenore Hirsch

Creative nonfiction presents a particular set of challenges to writers. In addition to knowing how to tell a story—including elements such as action, dialogue, scene, tension, and resolution—authors of this genre have to excavate their own lives for events and memories significant enough to have affected them personally and be of interest to their readers. They must then be willing to dive deep into the images and emotions related to their experiences and analyze their own roles in what happened, offering their unique perspective on real-life events.

Creative nonfiction writers must present themselves as characters on the page: vulnerable, authentic, and transparent. And they must tell the truth as they see it. In so doing, you, as reader, can connect with them on a personal level, viewing their experiences through their eyes.

Sometimes, this truth-telling detours away from memoir, from the story of the experience itself and into the sub-category of personal essay, in which the author attempts to find and communicate a greater universal truth in the kernel of lived experience. You are then invited to join the author in imagining the realms of possibilities that might spring from that kernel.

Whether written as memoir or personal essay, the topics in this section range from the rambunctious joy of childhood to travel adventures to speculations on the future of human evolution and everything in between. In the process, the authors explore ideas surrounding family, home, safety, growing up, relationships, politics, history, architecture, and more.

I hope you enjoy this selection of life-experience stories written by members of the Napa Valley Writers and polished for publication with the help of an amazing and knowledgeable editorial team—Kymberlie Ingalls, Paul Moser, and Peggy Prescott.

— Nonfiction Editor, Amber Lea Starfire

Acknowledgements

The *Opus IV Napa Valley Writers 2023 Anthology* we proudly present here is a true collaboration among our member authors, our genre editors and reviewers, and a professional publication support team that reaches beyond the Napa Valley writing community. As Managing Editor of our fourth Napa anthology, I have had the privilege to select and work closely with a dedicated editorial staff that transformed more than 60 electronic submissions in poetry and prose into this beautiful and expressive publication.

Poetry Editor, Antonia (Toni) Allegra; Fiction Editor, Lenore Hirsch; and Nonfiction Editor, Amber Lea Starfire; were our expert genre editors. They diligently led, managed, organized, and coached their own teams in the review, selection, and manuscript polishing process that is crucial to a quality publication. Their work was exceptional and made producing *Opus IV* a true collaboration.

I also want to acknowledge the professional manuscript assistance of Michael Jarvie (FixMyWords), our copyeditor, and Jo-Anne Rosen (Wordrunner), our book designer and formatter. Northern California photographer Bruce Fleming's beautiful and nuanced wine country image graces the cover of *Opus IV*.

Finally, I want to thank the Napa Valley Writers Board of Directors, past and present, for entrusting me with the position of Managing Editor of *Opus IV* and having the confidence in me to lead our signature publication. Lenore Hirsch, Amber Lea Starfire, Geoffrey K. Leigh, Kymberlie Ingalls, and Sarita Lopez shared their contacts, guidance, expertise, and experience with past anthologies. Their ongoing support throughout the lengthy process of bringing the Anthology to life and print was invaluable. Thank you all.

Contents

Poetry II • Beauties of Nature. 95

Poetry 1

Love and Relationships

Burying Ground

Marianne Lyon

I reverence this morning
Out kitchen window
grove of pines alchemies me
to family tombs
cemeteried decades on haloed hill

I exit from shadow thinking
Remember how Grandpa
vigored his daily walks
How Gram magicked every
Christmas Eve with
unexpected fairy surprises

Pilgrim myself back to Dad's
reverent eyes in incensed sanctuary
On way home from Mass
hear myself hum *Sanctus*
He croons back
This Little Light of Mine

Can't forget Mom's topaz eyes
Smile threads on her face
Her galaxy of love
still starlights my days

Morning splendors the room
I brushstroke these family memories
Begin to page my thoughts
for you to read
Grin lines my face
"This little light of mine,
I'm going to let it shine."

Americans in Paris

Nathaniel Robert Winters

I love the notion of her
Voice sounding so seductive
Like a saxophone playing jazzy Gershwin
On the bank of the Seine

Play tennis on red clay courts
Downy mist showing through her shirt
Ducking into shower, I soap her back
Watch bubbles circle the drain

Woman dresses for dinner
A goddess, making the most of her gifts
Blue bow in flame of red hair
Slit skirt shows stockinged leg

Perfume smells delicious
In the nape of her neck
Lilacs, roses and
Just a taste of cayenne pepper

Eyes peer into my soul
Deep green pools
Like sunny Mediterranean waters
Champagne open on the table

Je t'aime she says sensuously
We dance on the balcony
In the shadow of the Eiffel Tower
Fall back into bed, dinner will wait.

Why I Stole Your Pants

Justin Godey

Just there on the line. Hanging.
And there I was hanging out. Naked.
And there's a story. Dangling there.
With everything else. Dangling there.
See I was watching TV one evening.
In my pajamas drinking beer and breathing.
Vegetating, staring, not blinking.
When Ninjas broke into my living room.
I did what anyone else would do. I ran, like a deer, like a
    gazelle, like a cheetah.
Flying away on feet so fleet-ah. I took off on down the
    street-ah.
I wasn't watching where I was going to. I jumped onto a
    bus.
It turned out it was filled with old nuns that were going to
    Las Vegas, Nevada.
Who'd have thought-ah?
That sisters would want a romp in the old off-strip casinos
    too.
But I never made it to the City of Sin.
Because also on that bus there within was a lost ancient
    Doubloon.
That held the long-cursed soul of the dread red pirate
    John Devrola.
Who slaughtered thousands from Pensacola all the way to
    Saskatoon.
The ghost blew up that bus and burned my clothes and
    left me naked on the side of the road.
I walked until I heard a crowd and into the desert, I
    followed the loud sound of horns and bells.

Chanting and din and that's how I found myself
within the middle of an old-time Klan revival.
Like Burning Man, but gone all evil.
They all stopped and stared at my arrival. There were
werewolf Nazis on robot dinosaurs.
Supremacist ogres that howled and roared and men in big
white robes and crowns.
They looked less like wizards, and more like circus clowns.
They were all hateful and sexually repressed, and I was
standing there and I was undressed.
The crowd fell silent and stopped and stared, so I turned
and ran on out of there.
They screamed "Get 'em boys!" and oh the noise!
I don't tolerate Nazis on the best of days, and this was the
worst in so many ways.
So I ran with my knees to my chest. I took off to what I
thought was the West.
They had cowboy boots and I had bare feet, but I was
motivated by their white sheets.
I wracked. I ran. I kicked a bucket. I kicked a can. I left
them all in the dust.
Through the desert past burned-out cars and rust-belt
beltways.
I ran all day, I ran all night. Hopped a boxcar. Got myself
into a hobo fight.
He kicked my ass and demanded my money. I said, "I'm
broke and naked, I ain't got none, honey."
He said, "So sorry, no worry!" and then gave me some
money. Not a lot, enough for a cup of coffee.
So I found myself in Oakland, naked and broke and I'd
walk or hitch or even steal a bike.
But never found one that I liked. Hitchhiking naked, it's
pretty hard.

But with some charisma, newspaper, and cardboard I
    made it home.
I showered and went to bed. Woke up. Had breakfast.
Looked out my window ledge.
There before me on the line was a pair of pants that
    looked oh so fine.
They were too small. Maybe a little feminine.
I was home and had my own. But YOLO, y'know?
So then once again.
I Stole Your Pants.

The Slap

Emily Freiman

It wasn't just a little tap,
but a fiercely felt, delivered slap.
Came from way down deep, past his lap-
the little tap, a forceful rap.

The slap was meant to keep the tide
from swelling, feelings much too wide
to keep locked up, way down inside.
And all to do with love and pride.

'Twas for his Lady's honor, yes,
punish the man who dared transgress.
Backfire it did, and who could guess
his Oscar they might repossess.

Ah, such a harsh, reflexive act—
there is no way to take it back.

The meaningful deliverance.
It's done.
All acts have consequence.

Gone Girl

Kathleen Herrmann

Brewpub servers wear tired smiles, rush to reggae beat
I wait by the door
Green text bubble appears
Sorry mom, running late—be there in 10
NP:-) I reply

I don't know exactly how I lost you
Lunch twice a year, we were already distant
But you needed new boundaries, you explained
One text per year, no personal questions
Sushi slices laid between us, fleshy pink centers suddenly
   unappetizing
Staccato words pelted like hailstones
I memorized your back as you walked away

Our history loomed like towering monolith
I shrank from ghosts who made me watch
Homework meltdowns
Older sister's edgy teasing
Sullen glare from under hoodie
Twenty something and always too busy
I didn't want to take the hint

Solitary walks past young mothers at the park
Swing draws near then push, fly away, gleeful giggles
They cannot imagine hard stares, fiery words, final exit
If they could, would they care so much, do so much, try
   to do more?

Eighteen months

Fresh green text bubble
merry christmas
Careful words trickle, then big news
Can I meet him?
Here you come, your hand in his
I memorize your face as you walk toward me
One step at a time

Passions of the Heart

Marianne Lyon

Praise   wild
passion
fiery longings   raging songs unsung
free lurking hesitation   curious compulsion
ignite the set-aside   not-yet-concrete
laud shamans   magical spells   generals who inspire peace
priests who rouse devotion   children who believe they can fly
applaud wild fever that nudges us to rush to zesty gold mine
praise things we've always said we'd do   indulgences
we never thought we would   never thought we should
here's to making dithering useless   here's to kindling
that which makes no sense   that which doesn't rhyme
fit the meter what we cast   threw away
say no to parameters that suffocate
fear not dissonance   consonance will resound
ecstatically resuscitate your arduous beacon
enter locked secret room of vibrancy
congratulate passionate sun
within your heart   it may be love
lust   rage   determination
envy   heartache
exhaustion   joy
allow it to burn
its way
out

In The Kitchen

Yvonne Baginski

She tells me in the kitchen.
The sink, piled high with discarded dishes.
A stovetop covered in empty pots.
A celebration cake shredding chocolate crumbs into vanilla
    frosting.

Her voice shrill. Pitching pain ricocheted the walls and
    stormed the glass panes
The outdoor redwood deck protected in a dense, gray fog.

Something has happened.
She wants me to know.

Confusingly complex. She describes horror. My mind can't
    wrap around her words.

Spoon drowns in browned rice pilaf.
Knife cuts into a white sourdough loaf.
Fork stabs a red sliced tomato.

Living room voices drone and buzz. Laughing. Loud.
Fingers strum a guitar. A melody starts a song.
Oblivious to the damaged chaos on the other side of this
    shared wall.

Her father, she says, did what no man should. Ever.
We share blood, but not her story.

I loved him too. He was my trusted, daily lifelong
    touchstone. Now two years dead.

Empty green wine bottles reflect the harsh overhead light.
A candle flame wavers on the table.
The cracked window admits a slight breeze into the room.
The silver kettle whistles.

"Who's up for tea?" I ask loudly so the others can hear.
Thought expands time. One sentence crowding the other.
    She speeds up, finishing before another enters the room.
"Groomed from birth. He was a predator. I am scarred."
I stand alone in the kitchen, looking at the remnants of
    the last meal I will ever share with my family.
The room fills with strangers I have known all my life.
I pass out the mugs to pour the hot water for tea.

Who's Next?

John Petraglia

On a night when the sky
is so heavy with stars
it fills the overhead
with more than a hint
of the pearly streak
we rarely see these days
through the anthropomorphic haze.

The joy and awe I feel
from this starry brilliance
is not enough to dispel despair
about tonight's Supreme Court news
or Climate, or Trump still
or supremacist rampage
or this year's, yes, 204th mass murder
that will again not bring about
changes to gun control laws
despite outrages at political podia.

The more I adjust to the darkness
more stars come into view.
I try to think of them
as points of light among us
the next wave of those
who will fight the good fight
force desperately needed changes
that I no longer can
with my failing sight
and abdicating remorse.

Broken Up

Yvonne Baginski

Shattered shards of yearning litter the love-pocked
   landscape of my life.
Cracked
Smashed
Thrown
Snapped
Broken

Hoped-for fragments shattered by reality's grip.
Crystalline razors glisten, taunting touch. Beauty swept
   and trashed, so others will be saved.

Touch me,
Bring me back to life.
Make me whole.

Flesh slices. Drip. Drip. Drop.
A crimson stream forms, winding its way back to my heart.

By a Window in a Darkened Room

Jeffrey Kingman

and who is she
sends my head sparkling.

Sound of a kiss
   if lips rustled
like a dress
   or if water
a drop, or plop
   but a bird's song at night
                    doppler.

Her arms whisper
   shoulders rubbed distinct
anointed
   as from peppermint.

Pins of light
   stuck to the window.
Birds kiss out there
   they click, and clock.

No name
   just a cloud, receding.

Something black flies away.
   The night air
dims time.

Inside
   there's no vision.
Stars reflected in the touch
   evaporate.

—rustling of a dress
hurried footsteps—

Fledgling

Peggy Klick

After Mother died I
felt a flutter, over my right shoulder
but then her presence stopped;
startled, perhaps she wasn't
yet fully an angel

I imagine her hand over her mouth
not letting the gasp escape
which would be too much
for me and she; this
angel practicing, fledgling

Now she comes and goes
feathers against my face,
barely apparent, in rustling silence
she hovers; lingering hummingbird
a taste of sweet nectar.

Shoulder

Jeffrey Kingman

Family-challenged.
Young woman who protests
a manicured entryway
college hats and combs
bun versus tresses
                    sprouting.

Wheels polished
schools want a form
student eyes painted
or bloodshot. You write names
in French? That is
                    smart.

Bloodshot eleven o'clock
dancing at midnight
the boys will call you.
If girl feigns straplessness and
shows up late, it's
                    money.

You. Your lengthy earrings
shouldering on.
Dad says nothing. Teachers something.
Teachers behind lecture halls
bum cigarettes. Have you
                    a pack?

Brother won't save you. Look
over shoulder. Where is your money?
Kisses to bloody tongues. Your separation.
You're girl. Girlfriends are hard to find
though everywhere. But family
                              is in your face.

My BFF

Carole Malone Nelson

Bonded since birth, growing up together,
now growing old together.
Early morning walks
much slower, far shorter.
My BFF.

Never a disagreement or
even cross words.
Always in tune,
always on time.
My BFF.

Traveling the world together
following the sun,
sharing a love of desert,
mountains, beach.
My BFF.

Luminous blue sky, in want of a cloud,
sun rising low in the east.
Path turns west, she leads the way.
I'd follow her anywhere.
My BFF.

Graceful hands of a hula dancer,
slender torso,
ballerina's long, lean limbs,
No signs of aging.
My BFF.

Thick, black hair, not a strand of grey.
No wrinkles, broken veins,
sagging knees
or cellulite.
My BFF.

How easy to envy this avatar,
a much younger version
of Moi,
I muse with a smile.
My BFF.

Will I outlive her?
That remains to be seen.
I turn to the east leaving my shadow behind
until tomorrow.
My BFF.

Brown-Eyed Girl

Judy Baker

Fumbling first kiss
Sweaty summertime innocence
Freckled smile, sun-dried curls
Bikini tanned
Plastic transistor radio, tinny soundtrack
Anchored by "Brown-eyed Girl"
Flavors my teen-age romance

Half a century intervenes between then and now
Van the Man's gravel voice encases notes and rhyming
Syncopated timing
Simple lyrics, basic beat
Conjure summertime first kiss heat
Leaves me smiling
Blink of an eye
Memory like honey on my mind
Soft caress of gentle lips
Shy souls fumbling
Hearts synchronize to beat of butterfly wings
Awkward teen embrace, nose-bumping, virginal, sweet
Once-in-a-lifetime new

Fiction

Lightning Bugs

Rick Deragon

"Crickets," Jack said.

"What?" his mother asked from the kitchen as she arranged a pork chop on a plate.

"Crickets. I said, crickets. They're really loud tonight," he said.

"You can go listen to your crickets when you finish your dinner," she said, bringing a plate for her husband and a bowl of extra potatoes.

"Got your note about Cindy and her scout troop's overnight," Jack's father said, taking his seat. He unfurled his cloth napkin, placed it on his lap, and bowed his head.

Jack watched his lips move silently.

"How've you been, Jackie-boy?" his father said.

"I caught a mouse. Trapped it against a fence. He was tryin' to run away, but I stepped on his tail, then caught him."

"A mouse? A big mouse?" his father said.

"John, don't encourage him."

"Not really. Jus' a l'il one—like this," Jack said, cupping his hand to hold the imaginary mouse.

"That's mouse size, alright," his father said.

"Jackie, that's terrible. Those things are so dirty. He could bite you. John, talk sense to him."

"He wasn't gonna bite me. He was hurt."

"You're always getting into such mischief, worrying me to death," his mother said.

"Hurt?" his father said.

"He was bleedin'. His foot. I carried 'im in my sweatshirt pouch all day,"

27

"Oh, John," his mother said.

"What did you end up doing with him, Jackie?"

"Let 'im go after a while. Well, really, he just got away."

"Oh, the idea of carrying a rabies-infected creature all day. In your pocket. John, talk to him."

Jack's father studied his son's face. Jack ate a piece of carrot and cut a piece of the pork chop, but stopped after raising the fork just off the plate.

"He was probably scared, Jack, and he might have bitten you. They really don't like to be handled. After all, they are wild."

"Wasn't gonna hurt 'im."

"Go-ING," his mother said.

"Okay, go-ing. I wasn't go-ing to hurt him. Just wanted to feel how warm he was, his heartbeat."

"Jack, next time, let the little fella stay free," Jack's father said, taking another bite. "By the way, there are a few things I need to get after dinner. Want to come along?"

"Yeah—well, no. I was gonna go play. There's a lotta crickets tonight. An' lightning bugs."

"Go-ING," his mother said. "Go-ING."

"Okay, go-ing."

"I saw a sale on baseball gloves at Anderson's. Think we can make it before they close. Want a baseball glove? It's the season. But you'll have to try it on first. Come along?" Jack's father said.

His mother hovered over them with a plate of cookies. Jack reached for them, but she pulled the plate away and nodded at the remaining carrots. Jack forced the tines of his fork into a sliced carrot. He moved to eat it, but stopped short of his mouth, returning his fork to the plate where he impaled the remaining slices. This mass of pulp he gulped down at once, filling both cheeks like a squirrel.

"Dear God," his mother said.

His father looked down to hide his smile.

Jack gulped it down, snatched a cookie off the plate, and pushed away from the table in a flash of movement. "Bye."

He bounded off the back porch into a world that was as wide as the sea and as high as the highest cloud and twinkling star. The screen door slammed after him.

This world of possibilities that he roamed had dark night as its keeper and sunlight as its guardian. Twilight was its heart, dawn its soul. Into this world—his neighborhood—he entered and the realm of precious noises and sights revealed itself: of crickets chittering and frogs croaking, of rubber balls bouncing and bicycle chains clanking, of boys yelling and dogs yipping, of rain pattering on the asphalt driveway and the startling magic of the thunderclap.

To his left in the distance, Jack saw the houses of the neighborhood fading in the evening light. White, beige, gray, blue, yellow, or green, the houses stood in rows. Two-storied, wood-shingled, with brick and wooden siding, the houses formed a theme and variations—front picture windows on the right or left, front doors on the left or right, light colors accented dark houses, dark trim outlined light colored houses. Wrought ironwork or lathe-turned posts appeared on every other house's porch, and every facade had a full beard of shrubbery running from ear to ear. Personal touches punctuated each house—a picket fence, a half-buried wagon wheel, a miniature wishing well. The swelling twilight enveloped his neighborhood, and all these houses lost their details to the night, changed into dark shapes, evolved into pirate ships on the high seas, ominous castle keeps, cavalry forts on the hill, or enemy villages full of sharpshooters and evil.

Jack crossed the threshold of this dark and sultry twilight. He ran across the backyards as fast as he could. He felt the humid air beneath his shirt, and his heart racing after three backyards. He heard the wind rushing over his ears, and his sneakers making soft thumps on the lawns. When he stopped, the night had triumphed, and it was dark. In between his deep breaths, he heard the crickets calling back and forth.

Dark maple trees surrounded his friend's house, and Jack could see no window light between the limbs. He didn't even try tossing pebbles to the bedroom window, or even knocking on the front door.

Two streets over a shallow ravine separated properties, and trees and underbrush grew thick along its banks. A trickle of water always coursed along its way, and Jack knew he would find frogs there, and crickets, and lightning bugs. He ran.

Jack crawled under the lowest rail of a fence and looked back at the house on the hill. Standing stately against the sky, its second-story windows peered down at him like two big eyes. A jack-o'-lantern, Jack thought. He jumped to his feet and ran across the last part of the hill and flew into the trees along the ravine. He smelled the sweat of the creek bed, the perfume of honeysuckle, and the musk of milk-weeds and wildflowers. Fine twigs and branches slapped at his face as he slid to a halt next to the water.

There, Jack listened to the crickets chirping. He was sure they were assessing the danger he posed—his friendly presence against his potential for destruction. Then the frogs started up. They announced his arrival, too, and probably boasted of secret hiding places. Above, he watched the moon rise over the treetops to begin its march across the starry sky. Then he lowered his gaze and saw the lightning bugs.

His mouth opened in awe, and he felt a lightness bordering on flight. Like twinkling stars in a velvet sky, lightning bugs appeared and disappeared into the great silhouette of his neighborhood or the bulging profiles of trees. Mesmerizing, they floated through the darkness in shots of yellow and white, flashing here then there, shimmering as the highlights on a wonderful, unseen crown.

They were light, pure light, unconnected to the things of this world, the experience of light, of sight, captured in the simple darkness of this night.

Jack left the ravine and walked into a cloud of lightning bugs on the hillside. Holding out his hand, he cupped one after another, examining them as they crawled on his hand and up his arm. Some alighted, some lingered and flashed.

He knew just what to do. When a lightning bug flashed, he pinched it in half. The fleck of phosphorescent light, sticky and long, he placed on his knuckles as diamonds. He decided to put them inside jars when he returned home to have them as lanterns.

Jack wandered over the hillside collecting them. From ravine to jack-o'-lantern house, he caught more of the flying insects. He pinched them as they flashed, and after thirty minutes, he had filled his hands with the flecks of a diamond's luster. He sat in the grass studying the smears of glitter and shots of light in his palm. One by one, he picked them out and placed them in a line across his forehead and down his arms. *My crown of jewels*, he thought, *my shining cloak. I am the king of the ravine, the prince of the water, the duke of the hillside.* He stood up and marched across the hill looking left and right for his afterglow.

Then he remembered the hall mirror and yearned to see himself like this—lights out, sparkles on. So, he crawled under the fence and walked through the yards of the neighborhood—carefully, so he wouldn't be seen as an errant king or prowler. He crossed lots and streets, passed between shrubbery and trees. He thought of the dinner and his father's invitation to Anderson's. Maybe it wasn't too late.

Jack picked up his pace, recalling a time the previous summer when he sat with his father under the moon. The man explained the distance of the moon from earth, but it was too far for Jack to fathom. His father then told him about frogs, how they begin as fish-like swimmers, then lose their tails to become frogs. At that moment the lightning bugs appeared against the dark shapes of the neighborhood. Framed by trees and roof lines, the flashing insects appeared here and there, twinkling like signals from far away. They lit up with gentle, slow-blinking gold and white, and cast a spell across the yard. Their twinkling in thick and thin clusters gave the heavy cloak of nightfall a majestic air. Enchanted shadows everywhere glittered with gold.

Jack's father stood up and disappeared into that darkness. He walked back almost immediately and sat down next to his son. He held out his hand. Two lightning bugs crawled across his palm, flapping tiny wings, flashing their delicate lights.

"Watch, Jack."

His father picked up one, and when it glowed brightly, he pinched it. Jack heard a faint crunch. His father took the glowing tip and placed it on Jack's knuckle.

"There, you now have a fancy ring."

Jack then looked at his diamond-studded hands and arms, felt the sticky glue of the crown across his forehead. *I have to show him my costume*, he thought.

He trotted faster across the yards, watching his arms with their phosphorescent highlights swinging at his sides. He broke into a run.

Jack had to show his costume, tell his father about the frogs, and their language that Jack believed he understood. He wanted to tell his father about the crickets, and how the crickets had talked to him. He wanted to show his father the kingly crown and cloak and how he glittered in the night.

Jack's father stood next to the black sedan and looked around. He called out Jack's name, but not loud enough to bother the neighbors. The disc of the moon rose over the dark trees. The man heard crickets and smelled the damp and fertile night descend upon the houses up and down the street. He sat down on the padded bench seat. He turned the key and the car squealed and roared and then settled into a mechanical drone. He put the car in reverse and backed down the driveway.

Jack ran as fast as he could, spurred by the expectation of showing off his costume and the excitement of joining his father on the trip to the store.

He ran through a side yard and skidded on the grass as he made the last turn onto his street. A welling sense of desperation took hold of him. He worried that the lights on his crown and cloak might fade, that his father would not see them. He ran harder and faster, counting the houses remaining—six, five, four. Jack heard his father's voice, "There are a few things I need to get after dinner. Want to come along?" And he heard himself say, "No."

Confusion and desperation sickened him as he panted and ran. He wished he had said "yes" because he did want to go, but he had to go outside that night, too, for the crickets were so loud and so many, and the lightning bugs were enchantment itself.

Jack's father sat in the car at the foot of the driveway. He stuck his head out the car window and called, "Jackie" in the voice he used at the baseball games they organized in the corner field. It wasn't the calling of a name as much as a cry, a thick throated bark that shot into the night like a tribal incantation.

Jack knew the jewels on his crown and cloak would keep their glow long enough. *But will dad be able to see them?* He hurled himself around the curve of the street, and as he came to their next-door neighbor's house, he saw his father's car down the street. The red taillights of the Plymouth sedan glowed, and the right one blinked, and the bulky mass turned right and disappeared into the night.

The Farm

Richard E. McCallum

She grips my hand as we tiptoe past the door to the little room off the kitchen. As we stand in front of the pantry, we sparkle and steam, like icicles melting in the early morning sun. We move away from the passage leading up from the cellar, from which we came, located under the rambling farmhouse hidden in the deep woods of Massachusetts. "Shhhh ..." As we tiptoe, our weight does not transmit to the floorboards.

I kiss her.

Brilliant light beckons from orbs floating under the kitchen ceiling. Softer, smaller, golden globes flicker from century-old fixtures.

The mist swirls, and my grandmother appears. She carries a silver tea set, piled high with many empty cups made of fine Chinese porcelain with flower designs, and a large, now drained, teapot, of the same pattern. A ruffled apron covers her decorative holiday dress, and round wire-rimmed glasses frame intensely blue eyes.

"Hello, Grandma. Smells delicious in here," I say as Sarah moves alongside me.

"Richard? Oh, my. You've surprised me!" Gram places the tray down next to the ivory-white cast iron cooking range. Celestial powered radiant heat keeps the Thanksgiving side dishes hot. Lizzie, without physical strain, opens the heavy oven door, and the aromas rise to heaven. She checks the temperature and deems it adequate; the annual sacrifice to the Heavenly Father, for the blessing, received; the Mayflower colony at Plymouth Rock, and peace with the children-of-the-forest.

"Gram, I'd like you to meet Sarah." Elizabeth Delano-McCallum smooths her gray hair back and pins it into the tortoiseshell comb and moves closer.

"Just Sarah, Richard?"

She holds a steady French Huguenot blood stare into my spirit: I feel she searches for recognition of my commitment to Sarah.

"My girlfriend, Sarah." I feel under-dressed in my blue jeans and tee-shirt.

"That's better, Dear, what a lovely wisp of beauty." Gram primes the hand pump in the kitchen sink, and after three pumps, cold, clear refreshment spouts out. She fills a pitcher and places it in the icebox, on a tray over a cube of coldness.

"I love your glass figurines," Sarah directs our attention to the display.

Gram opens the frosted-etched glass cabinet doors and proudly shows off her collection of delicate figurines: a little girl ice-skating, a purple glass horse trotting, and a trio of dolphins leaping. I pick up a heavy metal miniature of the Eiffel Tower. Gram says, "Your Great Uncle Patrick was an ambulance driver in WWI and returned with many souvenirs from France." Other cabinets in the kitchen hold cherished items: dishes, bowls, cups, and glasses – all dating back to the turn of the century. A picture of Franklin Delano Roosevelt hangs between the cupboards. "Delano," I whisper to Sarah, "Gram's maiden name, she traces her family back to the Plymouth Colony; related to both FDR and Teddy Roosevelt."

"Yes, my Delano family spilled blood in these woods."

Spotty, my dad's dog, a black and white Collie-mix, charges in from outside, and startled by our presence, barks at us.

My Great Uncle John, who had been out with the dog, calms Spotty. He wears a worsted wool suit, tie, a fedora, and shiny black dress shoes. He introduces himself to Sarah; I note his breath smells of alcohol and cigarettes. I whisper to Sarah, "Gram forbids smoking and drinking in the house." Great Uncle John turns off his outdoor luminescence, hangs it on the wall with the others, and removes his hat.

Gram scrunches her nose and curls her lip in disgust, and glares at him. John cowers, "Is there anything I can do to help, Lizzie?" He replies as he removes his suit coat, loosens his tie, and rolls up his white dress shirt sleeves.

"Yes, you can pull the contribution out and bring it to the table. We," Gram collects me and Sarah, "will set the table. Be sure not to drop it, John." He turns away to avoid her eye contact.

Gram selects crystal glasses and puts them on the silver tray. "Richard, please bring the pitcher to the table." The reflective surface of the tray sparkles.

We enter the dining room where Victorian-era vapor lamps with cloth floral patterned shades and Tiffany glass covers illuminate the setting. Lace sheer curtains remain drawn on the windows framed by brocade drapes. My relations, all dressed in their Sunday best, gather for the feast. The adults find chairs at the long central table laden with steaming platters. My grandfather sits at the head, and I place the pitcher down next to him. The round table, being just the perfect distance away from over-attentive parents, attracts the children, and delightful chatter resounds. After the family settles, my Uncle Denny has us all pose for the traditional family picture just as his Uncle John staggers in with the offering.

"Granddad. Hi." I put my arm around my companion, "My girlfriend, Sarah."

"Your girlfriend? Well, what big news. How long have you two known each other?"

"We just recently met."

"Well, here's some advice from an ol' timer: take time to know each other, don't rush in. I courted your grandmother for neigh on a year 'fore I got my first kiss." He laughs.

"How long have you had this property?" Sarah inquires as we sit next to him.

"We bought it at the start of WWII; hoping to claim Richard's dad could be listed as 'needed on the farm' to avoid military duty."

"Did he qualify?"

"I don't know. Eugene ran off and enlisted before we even filled out the paperwork."

My mother approaches. She wears a beautiful green flowery full-length dress, the one I remember as her favorite. Effie May's reddish hair is combed back, revealing her high forehead, while wispy curls bounce down her neck. Effie displays her green earrings and a pearl necklace, an heirloom from the Delanos.

"Oh, Richard," she exclaims as she sits next to Sarah. "Our long-lost son has come home; so, to speak." She looks much healthier than during the sadness. Her smiling eyes lock with my girlfriend. "I am Richard's mom, Effie May."

"Pleased to meet you. I'm Sarah."

"Richard's lucky to have met you. Love strengthens all of us."

Grandpa continues as if he is the only person in the room. "Yes, we bought the farm from a drunk chicken farmer, then we went around the countryside and filled the place with what was on sale."

"Wow," Sarah says as she looks around the room.

"We bought fifty acres. The closest farm lays a few miles away."

"Did you farm here?" Sarah asks.

"We did one summer; raised some chickens; in the chicken coops below the barn. But, when the winter came, we sold them off and moved back to the Bridgeport, Connecticut area, where we were living. The farm reminds me of Ireland. But we're city folk at heart."

"Do you know the antiquity of this land?"

"We found Native American arrowheads, along with rock carvings indicating Viking expeditions. Some boards have square-headed nails. We believe they date back to the Plymouth Colony era. The stone walls defining the property were built centuries ago by early settlers. Old timber growth fell victim to lumber deforestation. Now, the trees number more than at the time of Columbus. Regrowth. Nothing dies here; everything renews."

"Amazing."

"A magical place, the enchantment based on family and shared history."

After the table is cleared, my uncles sit and talk politics. My right-wing Uncle EJ shouts support for the conservative issues, alongside my leftist Uncle Joe, who campaigns for the liberal. The women, Sarah, and I retreat to the little enclave with a player piano. The room features a small stone fireplace. Simmering light, from a mysterious source, bathes the flowers arranged in the colored glass vases decorating the room. A silver-plated framed portrait of Eleanor Roosevelt, a distant Delano link, hangs over the mantle.

One of my many aunts enters the room with a tray of shortbread cookies and tea. All the women and children gather around her. She notices us at once and places the plate down to introduce herself.

"I am Richard's Aunt Tin, Eugenia. Come, let us have some tea and cookies while we listen to the wax recording "Mine." My Aunt Mary's husband, Jack Casey, wrote the lyrics to this tune in the twenties. It was a hit in those days. He was shot down by mobsters who mistook him for his brother, a longshoreman with mob ties. His brother tried to avenge his brother's death but got killed as well. You know the Irish; the chain of revenge never ends."

We listen to "Mine," and then my Aunt Josephine, nick-named Wubbie, in the Irish tradition of never using the real name, winds up the player piano, and inserts sheet music. The piano plays itself, with each key compressing as she pre-tends to play. We sing along with the familiar tunes.

My third Aunt, Aunt Sis, notices we are tired and says, "let me show you the bedrooms so you can settle."

"Thank you," Sarah says, yawning.

"We will be sharing the bed, Sarah." Sis says, "Hope you don't mind."

Sarah looks at me with sparkling eyes and says, "That's fine."

"Where am I going to sleep?" I ask.

"Anywhere away from her." My Aunt laughs.

I warm, and Sarah giggles.

Aunt Sis illuminates the way up the stairs. The old, creaky, wooden stairs do not make any noise. She escorts us into the first bedroom overlooking the garden and the hand-drawn water well. A half-moon back-lights skeletal tree branches, blowing in the wind as rain clouds pass. My Aunt frumps the feathered pillows and pulls back the worn but loved hand-made quilt. A Classic Victorian dresser with a full mirror sits at the side of the bed, and an ivory-handled hairbrush and bone comb await their use. Our lights reflect-ing in the mirror brighten the room.

We drift through the passage on the second floor, an A-framed low ceiling with its slanted walls cluttered with beds, over-stocked bookshelves, framed pictures, and an odd collection of collectibles. "The children sleep up here. The bachelors will slumber in a chair or sofa downstairs. We single females will bed together. The couples will make use of the bedrooms."

"How many bedrooms are there?" Sarah asks.

"As many as needed, dear."

At the end of the chamber, an opening offers access to a passage. My Aunt says, "Now, Richard, you show Sarah the privies, but you behave like a gentleman; any complaint, and your mother will hear of it."

"I promise, Aunt Sis." I hold Sarah's hand.

"I'll make sure he behaves, Ma'am," Sarah says as she tightens her grip.

I whisper, "Her real name: Elizabeth: Sis; her nickname."

Sis leaves, and I open the door and lead Sarah down a narrow old stairwell. It descends to a little "in-between shed" betwixt the farmhouse and the two-story barn. This storage room contains tools and items you could not decide whether to put in the connecting barn or stow in the farmhouse.

The multiple pathways in the barn are demarcated by the collections alongside. Bats startled by our glow fly past us and into the farmhouse, causing chaos and panic among the celebrators. We navigate through the assemblages: old cars, a movie projector from the forties, stacks of pictures still framed, steamer trunks full of silk outfits, National Geographics dating back to the 1920s, and early turn-of-the-century machines and tools. The smell reeks damp and musty. Our brilliance reflects off the pupils of living creatures who stare at us before scampering away. Each footstep navigates over old wooden planks, the support level unknown. Ladders lead up to rafters, but who dares to climb to the summit? A hoarder's dream of heirlooms awaits the collector of needful things. We make it to the outhouse, or commodes, as they are really "in house," being stationed at the very end of the barn. Three holes carved out of the wood structure provide for the family to sit together. A large diameter oval and another of medium size sets about two feet off the floor, and a small circular opening allows access for children. Sarah transverses through the swinging door. "I wish you, me, and a child of ours could sit together here." I, respectfully, hold a dim night light just outside. She comes out and proclaims, "I lost the need."

After the tour of the barn, we ascend using the old, narrow way. We pass through without interruption. Heading towards the room assigned to Sarah, we notice the door alongside lurks ajar.

"Who sleeps in there?" She questions.

"My grandparents. 'Grandad gets too frisky,' Grandma says, 'to have anyone sleep in there with us.'"

Sarah laughs, "Well, good for the old folks."

We peek in the room and see delightful antiques. On the table, next to the bed, the book, *The House of Delanos*, lies open to the chapter about the Plymouth Colony. Alongside, on the bedside shelf, the McCallum bible footnoting the McCallum history awaits inquiring fingers.

We cross to the window and watch the rain. As we glide out onto the window A-frame: thunder roars and lightning flashes. Our souls wash clean. We look down on the front lawn where the apple tree, hit by a bolt, remains alive. Distorted and splintered, its offshoots still produce fruit, a replenishable life.

'Twas the night after a day, and on the lawn under the old apple tree, Sarah asks, "Why do we return?" Lightning bugs swarm about us, and the insects' flashes define our presence. "We offended the spirit of the land. We desecrated my family's history, home, and people."

"We were stupid, partying, teens." Her light has grayed over the decades; however, she looks beautiful in a full-length flowering dress, hair brushed back, and decorative jewelry.

"You and I shamed Grandma's bed, and our 'friends' ran-sacked this place." My light beams thinner than when I was younger, but I stand tall in my suit and polished shoes.

"I didn't even know your last name." Her light reddens. "I remember we went out on the roof, and it was raining." She whirls a bit, "We danced naked."

"A bolt of lightning hit the tree. Knocked us off the roof."

"Try the front door again, Richard."

We walk to the entranceway and knock; the power within sparks. No response. The passage remains inaccessible. As we start to take the route to the cellar, Sarah says, "We have been coming here every Thanksgiving for what? A long time? We have progressed. Haven't we, Richard?"

"Yes, I commit to you."

"And me you, and I love and respect all of them."

The front access opens, and the celebration of grateful-ness and companionship radiates out into the cold dark. My father appears in the doorway.

"So nice of you and Sarah to join us. I just got here myself, after a long delay. I opened a room for you two."

We shine.

Bear's Valley

Joan Osterman

I've lost my bearings in a maze of cul-de-sacs, dragged by a mud-colored mutt at the end of the leash. The midday sun shimmers off the sidewalk—and a breeze, instead of cooling, makes it even hotter.

"Bear," I call out, "I sure hope you know how to get home." The husky mongrel pulls me down one street after another. Bear is my cousin Alan's dog. Visiting him in San Jose, I feel sorry for Bear, whose owner lacks patience for odor-sniffing meanderings, so here we are.

"One more block, then we're going home. . . OK, around the corner, then we're turning back." I lose every attempt to negotiate with the dog, and finally give in. "You know your neighborhood, where the good smells are; we'll go home when you're ready."

Every street looks alike—tract homes with beige or tan vinyl siding, groomed lawns with sculpted shrubs. Not even a cheeky dandelion peeks through. We approach a house with variegated stone pillars in front, topped with the twisted trunks of bonsai trees. But as we draw closer, I see the stone is concrete; the plants are plastic.

We wander for a mile or two. Though cars whiz by, not a soul walks or plays on the sidewalk. No one mows the lawn or works in the garage even though it's Saturday. Likely they are sealed inside their climate-controlled homes.

With no cell phone, I'm at the mercy of this animal. My mouth is parched, my damp t-shirt clings, and the leash handle digs into my skin. Why didn't I bring a bottle of water?

The pup's pink tongue hangs partway out. "Wouldn't you like to head home, have a nice drink?" Bear stares up at me, brown eyes appealing; he pants, and plows forward.

The dog abruptly turns into a narrow alley, overgrown with wild morning glory and lamb's quarters. I scan the area, wonder if we're trespassing. Bear stops in front of a half-acre of knee-high weeds and grasses, lush between trees laden with ripe golden peaches—remnant of an orchard. Birds flitter between branches.

In the chain link fence surrounding the grove, there's a person-sized gap where the wire mesh has been pulled apart. No one's around, so the dog and I slip inside.

I rest on a wooden step stool under the leafy canopy, breathe in the fragrance of ripe peaches. Bear lies down beside me. "What a beautiful, thick coat." I drape my arm on his back and run my fingers through the dense fur on Bear's neck folds.

When I close my eyes, a fertile valley spreads out around me—millions of trees, family farms—almonds, apricots, peaches, pears, cherries, blooming pink and cream every spring. Kids pilfering ripe fruit. Farmers coaxing bounty from the earth, shipping crates worldwide.

High voices and laughter interrupt my reverie (bring me back). Five or six kids appear; a lanky blond girl climbs a tree and starts picking, handing fruit down to her buddies, who stuff their backpacks. A boy with warm dark eyes offers me a few golden peaches. "What's your dog's name? Can I pet him?"

"Bear. Let him sniff your hand first."

The boy giggles. "He's bigger than you." He hugs the dog, resting his chin on Bear's head. "Some birds pooped in Ryan's hair," he tells me, nodding towards another boy.

They take off on their bikes. I bite into the luscious fruit, savor it while rivulets of juice stream down my chin. The dog's gaze stakes his claim, and I split off half the peach. Bear gulps it in one mouthful, and we share the next peach, too.

We're in no hurry to leave our sanctuary. "Imagine roots breaking down the concrete, trees pushing up through the pavement—orchards taking the valley back, block by block," I whisper to Bear, stroking his silky ears. "Imagine petals falling in spring, covering the ground like snow."

Bear and I breathe in the air, heavy with fruit, lazing until an older boy's voice intrudes. "Ma'am, are you okay? It's awful hot."

"Just fine," I smile, and ask directions.

"Let's take the last peach back to Alan." I wink at Bear, "unless we get hungry along the way."

Sushi

Brad Shurmantine

It was a mistake bringing him here. Tommy was squirming in his seat. They should have gone to Sizzler or KFC, where Tommy knew the food and felt at home. Why did he choose a sushi restaurant?

Because he wanted the meal to be special, something Tommy did with his dad. They'd had a great day already, a memorable day. They went to the train museum and walked through the capitol building. They got ice cream at a cool little shop in the Historic District. They found a toy store and he bought Tommy another action figure and a skateboard. Sharon would probably not let him use the skateboard; she worried too much about the boy, that he would fall off and break his arm. So he told Tommy they would keep the skateboard in his car for now, Tommy wouldn't tell his mom about it, and he would only ride it when his dad was with him.

"Next week we'll go to a skateboard park," he told his son. "And I'll teach you how to ride it."

But now they had to get through dinner. Tommy had to be home by eight.

"Tommy, sit down, Honey. Stop squirming around."

"What is this place?" Tommy sat down but kept twitching.

"It's a Japanese restaurant. Has your mom ever taken you to a Japanese restaurant?"

"No."

"Good. This will just be something you and me do. I think you'll love Japanese food."

"What is Japanese food?"

46

"It's rice and vegetables and fish. It's very delicious."

"I want a hamburger."

"Honey, we went to McDonalds for lunch. We can't have hamburgers again." He had to stop calling him "Honey." Fathers shouldn't call their sons "Honey."

"I don't like rice and vegetables."

"Yes you do. You ate rice all the time when me and Mommy were together. And you have to eat vegetables. Vegetables are good for you."

"But I want a hamburger."

"You're not getting a hamburger. I just told you. Let's look at the menu and see all the good stuff they have. Open your menu."

Tommy opened his menu but didn't look at it. His eyes were darting all around the restaurant. He couldn't read, and there were no pictures of food in it, so there was no point in him opening the menu. But he pretended his son was following along as he read aloud and tried to find something the boy might like. Maybe this would teach Tommy something about how menus work.

"OK, on this first page are appetizers. That's something you eat right away, while they're fixing your dinner, something to munch on. Should we order an appetizer?"

"I don't know."

"I think we should. Look, there's all sorts of funny things here. Crazy Dragon Ball. Monkey Brain." He looked up, hoping to see his son smile, but Tommy frowned instead.

"It's not really monkey brains. They just call it that. It's fried mushroom with tuna and crab. Should we order some Monkey Brain?"

"No!"

"Yeah, I don't think we should." It was too expensive anyway. He scanned through the choices, looking for something the kid might like. Tommy might like playing with some of this food, like the mussels. Maybe he'd get a kick out of cracking them open.

"Look, they have tempura. That's like french fries only there's vegetables inside. Let's order some."

Tommy looked blankly back at him, still unexcited by this new adventure.

"What should we order for dinner? You like chicken. Chicken Katsu—that's just like KFC. Does that sound good?"

"OK."

"It comes with rice. I remember you eating rice all the time. You can put some ketchup on it."

The Chicken Katsu cost sixteen bucks. He should have taken him to KFC. The waitress came and he ordered sushi and California rolls for himself, and a large sake. This meal was adding up. It was more than he could afford, but he only got to see his son once a week. He ordered a large Coke for Tommy.

"So. You've never been to a Japanese restaurant. They use chopsticks. Do you know how to use chopsticks?"

"No. I've seen them. At Panda Express. But I don't know how to use them."

"I'll teach you."

He took Tommy's hand and placed the chopsticks between his little fingers and showed him how to pinch the tips together. Tommy seemed to be getting it. Then they practiced picking up a bag of sugar from the tabletop, and Tommy wasn't getting it at all, and got very frustrated. Everything about being a parent was hard.

"It's OK, Honey." *Stop calling him Honey*, he thought. "Maybe your hands are too little. We'll get a fork. It's OK."

He wondered if the restaurant had crayons or something for kids to play with, and looked round to see what the other kids were doing. But there weren't any other kids.

"Hey, we haven't talked about school yet." Tommy had just started kindergarten. It had been another battle, because he thought the school district where he lived was much better. "Do you like school?"

"It's OK."

"What do you do?"

"We read stories, and play. And count. And make pictures."

"Do you like your teacher? Do you like Miss Rogers?"

"Yeah, she's nice."

He had met Janice Rogers at the parent conference in October. He drove all the way from Berkeley, where Diane lived. After he left Sharon, he moved in with her. A long drive for a ten-minute meeting. Tommy took his hand and showed him his cubby and his desk, and what was in his desk. Nothing, really. Tommy showed him the fish he had painted that was on the bulletin board with all the other fishes, the kindergarten school of fish. Then they all sat together and Miss Rogers told them that Tommy was a very good student. He was very friendly. He played well with all the children and seemed to especially like story time. She told them nothing, really. She was very young, and he wondered if she knew what she was doing.

"So, who are your friends?"

"Umm. Neil. Suzanne. Kara."

"Who's your best friend?"

"Umm. I guess Neil. I went to Neil's birthday party."

When did that happen? Who was Neil? He couldn't picture this Neil kid.

"Did you have fun?"

"Yeah! We played games and had ice cream and cake. It was a Guardians of the Galaxy party. We saw *Guardians of the Galaxy*."

"Really? Did you like it?"

"Yeah, I liked it. I liked Rocket. He's a raccoon."

"What was the movie about?"

"I don't know. It was kind of confusing. I don't know what it was about."

"You don't know what it was about at all?"

"Well, there was this evil guy trying to get back the orb Peter Quill stole."

"The what?"

"The orb. It contained all the power of the universe. Whoever had the orb controlled the universe. I don't want to talk about it."

The waitress brought them their coke and sake, and their tempura. He asked her for a bottle of ketchup.

He watched with satisfaction as Tommy explored his food, dipped the tempura onions into the ketchup and ate thoughtfully. He loved watching Tommy eat. He looked healthy and clean; his clothes were nice. Sharon was a good mother. But there was something about Tommy that worried him. He just didn't seem happy or adventurous enough, like a boy should be. He wasn't embracing this new experience, this new food. Why did he have to put ketchup on everything?

Tommy pushed his plate away. "I don't want anymore."

"You haven't eaten much."

"I'm full."

"Here, eat this. I think it's a sweet potato."

"I'm full, Daddy. I don't want any more."

"You told me you were hungry and I ordered all this food. Now you're going to eat it. Eat this sweet potato."

Tommy gave a huge sigh and took the chunk of sweet potato and stirred it around in his ketchup. Then he brought it to his mouth and took a tiny bite of it.

"Eat it."

He continued nibbling, getting ketchup all over his mouth.

"There's no dessert unless you eat your dinner. You know the rules."

Tommy popped the rest of the potato in his mouth, chewed and swallowed it silently, and drank some Coke.

"So. You're spending every afternoon with Grandma?"

"Yeah. She picks me up every day and brings me home until Mommy gets home."

"Is that fun? Do you have fun with her?"

"Yeah. It's Grandma."

"What do you do?"

"She reads me books. I play with my toys. Daddy! Grandma got a trampoline for our backyard! She just got it. Me and her jump on it together."

A trampoline. Why wasn't he told about that? Those things are dangerous.

"Really? That sounds like fun." He should have gotten a trampoline. Of course, he had no place to put it. Sharon got the house, and her mother had a house, but after things fizzled out with Diane he had to move to a two-bedroom apartment. When they had Tommy and bought that house, the only thing he demanded was a big backyard where he and Tommy could someday play ball. That first evening in their new home he stood on the patio, drinking a beer, and imagined Tommy running out for a pass. *Go long, Tommy. Go long.*

"It is. Grandma's teaching me how to jump on it."

The waitress brought the rest of their food.

"This is miso soup. Do you want to try it?"

"I don't like it."

"You haven't tried it. You don't know if you like it or not."

"I don't want soup. I just want to eat my chicken."

"Try the soup. Just a taste."

He took the ceramic spoon and stirred the soup around and took a spoonful and held it in front of Tommy's face.

"Try it."

"I don't want to."

"Just try it. Just a little taste of it." He thrust the spoon against Tommy's lips.

He took the smallest possible sip, and then frowned and leaned back. "I don't like it."

"You didn't really try it. You have to try things."

This was just the kind of thing that made him feel desperate sometimes. He had no hold over Tommy. Tommy was skittish and nervous around him and just seemed afraid of everything. He wasn't growing up to be a strong, confident boy. If Tommy lived with his father, he would be having new experiences all the time. He would be learning how to play all kinds of sports. They would hike and go climbing. He imagined Tommy ruddy-faced and breathless, running up the trail ahead. But those women didn't know what a boy needed.

They ate in silence for a while. Tommy lathered ketchup over everything.

"Does your mom ever talk about me?" he suddenly asked.

"No."

"She never says anything?"

"No." He thought for a while. "She wanted me to have fun today. She said we would have fun."

She had loved him so much. The years before Tommy was born, they had been crazy about each other. They went to Italy. She was such a pal. That boat ride they took to Corfu, from Brindisi. They didn't have much money then. It was a warm evening and they decided to buy deck tickets. They stood among all the other kids with backpacks and when they were allowed to board, he fought his way through, left Sharon behind. He found a bench on the main deck and spread out their stuff, and she soon joined him. It was such a warm night as they headed out. They sat on the bench and broke out bread and wine and cheese, kissed and looked at the stars. Their whole life was before them, and they had each other, and Italy, and now Greece. She slept on the bench and he slept on the deck beneath her. But within an hour they were pulling out all their summer clothes and putting them on. It got so cold, and the wind was biting, and the engines were loud. They barely slept; they were miserable.

They got to Corfu at dawn, exhausted, but found a little hotel, took hot showers and went to bed, slept for hours. Woke up, made love, went out and rented a motorbike. She got on the seat behind and wrapped her arms around him. By two o'clock they were lying on the beach at Giali, looking at all the topless Germans, the tall, beautiful Scandinavians. Giving them names. *Aranciata. Rosina.* Whatever color their bikini bottoms were. Sharon was topless too, lying on her back, soaking up the Greek sun, her eyes closed behind her sunglasses, her nipples out for everyone to see. She was more beautiful than any of those Germans. His wife.

"Daddy, can we go?"

"Yeah, we can go." He signaled to the waitress and she brought the check. "We still have an hour. We could go get some dessert. Or, you know what? We have enough time to go buy a helmet and do some skateboarding. Do you want to do that?"

"Yes!"

They left the restaurant in a good mood, ready for one more adventure. They made a quick trip to Walmart and bought an inexpensive helmet, then headed downtown to the skate park.

The park was nearly deserted; just a couple teenagers practicing tricks. He found a flat place and set the skateboard down and Tommy watched.

"You just get on and get balanced and push yourself along." He showed Tommy how it was done.

"Now you get on."

He held Tommy's hand as his son stepped carefully on the board. He held both Tommy's little hands and pulled him along for a few feet.

"See? That's what it feels like. For now, just practice getting on and off the board. Balancing yourself. Once you have the hang of it you can push yourself along."

He found a bench and sat down and watched Tommy try to balance on the skateboard. He kept falling off and getting back on.

Tommy looked up and a huge grin flashed across his face and arrowed into his father's heart. Scott was suddenly crushed by love for his little boy. It swamped him. He felt helpless in its wake. He never chose this love. It claimed him, swallowed him up. He chose to love Sharon. He chose Diane. He never chose this.

The Drone Massacre

W.P. Paul

Far, far away from our home planet Earth, a tiny and close to Earth-size orb known as the planet Tre blasts through the empty space around its star, rotates at the bottom of its gravity well, and provides a habitat for seven billion of our human siblings. Nine months ago, and at a time parallel with our seemingly endless goodbye to the COVID-19 pandemic, a brutal atrocity was perpetrated on that distant world. This barbarism became known as The Drone Massacre and ignited a series of events that shook the lives of every child and adult on Tre over the ensuing months. Lela, a freedom marcher, was standing near the front of the killing ground when the slaughter commenced.

If you were gazing toward her corner of the cosmos at that time, I hope you sent some love. She needed it.

The crack-thump, crack-thump of mechanized weapons fire struck Lela's eardrums with the force of hammer blows. The rapid puncture and dismemberment of the human flesh around her triggered something in her brain that dissociated and disoriented her. Before the bloodletting, she had been standing with her fellow protestors in Patriot's Square in front of City House in Ghonjerdad City. Then her mind leapt three steps back from her body and into a midnight fog. In less than a second, her subconscious had erected a barrier between her and reality, and this protection mechanism only allowed glimpses of images, sensations, and thoughts through gaps in the dark, numbing mist.

The roar of guns and screams faded to the volume of lion chuffs. She felt vertigo, then realized she was falling. Her eyes fixed on the flashes from machine gun muzzles that twinkled on the polished steel skin of what appeared to be giant metal soldiers. Then a Luna Cow sweatshirt blocked her view. The black sweatshirt depicted a cartoon cow, outlined in white, with black and white hair and a pink udder and nose. She felt awe in the presence of the cow. Her brain ached to determine its meaning. It dawned on her that she and the body that wore Luna Cow now lay on the ground. The cow glowered at a cartoon depiction of Luna, the planet Tre's sole moon. The caption read "No! You Jump!"

That doesn't mean anything! Lela thought and raged with the urge to rend Luna Cow's teats, legs, and tail from her body.

Doesn't matter, she told herself, and the anger ebbed. *Just an odd sweatshirt on someone . . . who, who cares? But how could I forget that fucking cow! . . . Oh!*

It clicked.

She recovered images of her fellow peaceful and unarmed protestors being brutalized and strewn across the square.

A pang of shame over her rage at the cow and disregard for the person who had donned the bovine caricature tightened her throat. Then a nagging certainty that she was forgetting something else important jabbed her gut and injected two pumps of bile.

She registered a stab of pain in the back of her head, touched it, and felt a bump, but she did not remember a collision. She tasted copper in her mouth, probed with her tongue and felt viscous blood. She winced when the tip of her tongue hit gouges inside her right cheek. Her eyelids drooped with a weight akin to thirty-six hours with no sleep.

Lela willed her eyes open and realized she could no longer hear drone fire.

She heard a wail to her left, and located a woman rocking on her knees and clutching the spurting stump that had been her left arm with her right hand. Lela felt a twist in her gut and looked away.

There's something I should tell her to do. Something with a 'tee' or an 'or' sound. What is it?!

An unrelated image pushed into her mind. She saw Davu standing next to her before the onslaught. They'd gaped at the three-meter-tall metal monsters that had taken up positions facing the crowd, twenty-five meters in front of them and halfway down City House's stone stairs.

Were people in those things? . . . and his left hand was in my right. Right? . . . Yeah.

Her jaw clenched with the shock and shame that she had forgotten Davu. She searched and found his motionless body lying two meters out of reach. She could only see the back of his green hoody with the hood down, the back of his head, and his left arm. The fingers were splayed and the wrist was bent at an unnatural angle. She longed to watch him breathe but could not see his chest or belly.

Lela realized her legs were numb when she tried and failed to roll to her side and run to Davu. Her eyes wrenched wide at the sight of three lifeless human bodies in a criss-cross stack that pinned the lower half of her body. It had been obvious that something was wrong with her brain, but not this wrong; not unable-to-register-the-pressing-weight-of-dead-people-wrong. In her conscious experience, it was as if the oozing bodies had just materialized on top of her pelvis and legs.

She pushed, then pounded at the bodies, but could not move them. She planted her left hand and twisted towards Davu.

"Davu . . . Davu! . . . Daavuu!"

No reply.

A gush of acid in her stomach reminded her that yelling was unwise. Sudden exhaustion pricked and then punctured her muscles. She fought each incremental droop of her eyelids, then the loll of her head, and the twist down into unconsciousness.

When she snapped awake, her heart rate and terror crescendoed and conjured the vision of a series of small chunks of grey cottage cheese brain matter pulsing out of her ears. The fact that it was impossible for her to see anything coming out of her own ears was no comfort.

Wait. I was just pretty darn sure about something impossible . . . That's scary. Probably insane . . . I'm pretty sure, it's impossible . . . Yeah. I can't see my ears . . . feeling for chunks . . . thank God, no chunks.

She looked around for something to anchor her, but only saw immobile, dead, dying, or maimed bodies. She knew there was advice that could calm her but could only register an inkling of it.

In . . . Invent . . . Inventory the facts. That's . . . I think that's . . . it.

One fact was that Balahsia, the authoritarian empire which controlled roughly half the landmasses of the Planet Tre, had opened fire on its citizens, including Davu, and her. Lela felt certain that such an atrocity had never happened before. *But what did Davu say?* "They erase the history they don't want us to know." She mulled this statement over. It didn't feel like paranoia anymore.

They will erase the whole massacre and the memory of our lives. She mourned. *But, that secret network. Davu said. Lowest caste's glances and hushed double-meanings . . . . Hope it spreads by hushed glances . . . hushed glances . . . I like that I'll tell Dav-"*

Her heart ached. She could not tell Davu anything.

She thought about yelling at Davu again, but her neck

muscles locked and refused to turn. Her thoughts spiraled. *Don't look. Don't feel it . . . Danger not to. Don't want to. Crazy not to. Pay attention or die! Stop! Try something else.*

Lela screwed her eyes shut, scrunched her entire face, and visualized Davu squatting, turning, finding her, and helping her push the corpses off her body. She willed their escape to the small clearing in the woods near the bank of the Shantu River where they had first met when she was still sixteen and he was seventeen.

She was transported by the earthy scent memory of the clearing floor and its foundation of brewing humus, cover of fresh leaves, and dots of mushrooms. The rich odor was held in place by an inner perimeter of cold-resistant manga and banana trees and outer boundary of maples and oaks. This affiliation of flora cast layers of shadows on the heart of the glade. The first time Lela touched Davu's right cheek and the first time she ran her fingers through his hair. Both happened as they lay under the cover of shadows where they felt safe and could watch the river but not be seen from it.

Lela convinced her mind that she was by the river, safe and invisible. She luxuriated in the memory for seconds? minutes? Then the helplessness of being trapped under cadavers pressed back into her consciousness.

Damn it! She groped for another distraction. *Savage nations! No, that's a slur. Davu's illegal book says "United" something. Free Nations that's it. Democracies with universal rights and . . . what was it? Ahhhh oth—other good things. We need.*

Lela visualized United Free Nations nine rotor whirly birds landing in front of City House's stone steps. In her imagination, fifty-four med techs exited each aircraft. She knew the aircraft were much too small for that number of people and pictured the techs stacked like logs in the woodshed at her family's lake cabin. She imagined the voices of rescuers.

This one over here. Priority one.

I'm a medic, sir, need to put pressure on that wound. Sorry. It'll hurt.

How many fingers am I holding up ma'am?

Wishing did not make rescuers appear.

If they do come, it will be another war. Whole planet again. Decades of truce. Poof.

A fantasy took hold. Lela watched herself jump into the air, transit three thousand miles of ocean in three seconds, fly over the U.F.N., and rally the billions to the aid of herself and her comrades by projecting commands through her megaphone mouth. "Come help now! But don't invade!"

I'm squattin' in the crazy prairie, Mom. . .

Lela sought refuge in a favorite memory from when she was four and toddled over to her mom's desk. Her mom's eyes were sharp and focused on her work and then crinkled with smile lines when they turned and looked at Lela.

"The sharp is how to work and the crinkle means love." Lela whispered her mantra about that moment. The feeling of safety words engendered was fleeting.

Her mind shifted to last night's argument with Davu. Both had asked and then insisted that the other not attend the march, but both attended anyway.

Idiots.

Caste-mixed relationships like Lela's and Davu's were illegal in the Balahsia and therefore hidden by necessity. All the marchers wore masks to conceal their identities, and for Lela and Davu the masks also concealed their illegal connection. Lela looked and located her mask on the ground, perhaps a meter away. The forehead of her mask was touching the chin of Davu's and the eyeholes of their masks looked into each other. Moments of looking into Davu's eyes flashed through her mind. The first time in the clearing his eyes were filled with defiance despite a touch of fear. From the back seat of the limo, she caught Davu's eyes in the rearview mirror, and his focus on the job could not completely mask his tenderness. In bed in her apartment, where, for moments, their eyes connected and only the safe and warm cocoon of their love existed.

She took a deep breath into her belly until it expanded against a body. Her skin convulsed at the touch of three degrees too cold, and dead flesh, and pushed a breath out fast.

Don't think about that.

She reached and grasped the chin of her mask with her fingertips and pulled. Instead of dragging towards her as expected, her mask flipped in the air and knocked Davu's mask out of sight. She craned her neck and stretched her gaze until exhausted, but did not find it. Lela felt the sting of new tears and pulled her mask over her face.

She struggled to comprehend the boil of impressions and feelings in her mind. Then a conviction came into focus.

Alive now does not mean alive in an hour or minute.

Lela felt a burst of panic and strength. She squirmed, pushed, and tried to slither out from under the cooling corpses that continued to press down on her numb pelvis and legs. She failed. She panted.

Images of a lion with a blood-mottled mane, smashing against cage bars and then collapsing looped in her brain. The images somehow both horrified and cooled the burn of anxiety, or at least distracted her. Then the lion disappeared, left her to boil, and a different synapse fired, or something broke, or both. She felt a vague awareness that choosing to survive at this moment could cost her sanity. She chose it anyway.

Manic humor dislodged her fright.

This is ridiculous. Everything about me is ludicrous! I spent time on . . . what? Calculus or marketing!?! Bangs or no bangs!?! Where to apply to school?!? I'm absurd!

Countless hours mourning you, Mom! Pissed at Dad for, I don't know, disconnecting?

I'm a ridiculous person.

Her growing mirth felt like she was faking hysterical laughter for a joke she did not get; however, it did accomplish one critical task. Her heart no longer raced, or at least she could not feel it. It felt like control.

Alive now does not mean alive in an hour or minute.

"Yeah. Thaaaat's helpful." Lela muttered in a whisper.

She felt an unhinged laugh well up from her belly. Survival still being the point, at least for the moment, she suppressed the laugh and waited with her mouth in a grin that failed to touch her eyes.

Someone will come. Luna cow. No . . . wait for—I . . . I . . . I'll . . . I'll know. I'll. I'll know it! I'll know it.

"Tourniquet!" she blurted before she could stop herself. She searched for the woman with the hemorrhaging arm. Then she heard whirring and crunching sounds somewhere behind her. She twisted her sore neck to its limit but could not find the source.

"Tick tock! Roll 'em in. Clean up the bodies," a voice commanded.

A chill climbed her spine. She clenched every muscle from her toes to her nose until her mind turned the metallic chirps of rolling machinery into mouse squeaks.

I should throw some cheese. She thought and nodded.

She heard a groan. *From Davu?* She stared and thought she saw his body move.

"Davu. Honey. Train's coming. Stop your l'il game. My pup-py." No response. She lay back.

"Puuuppy puppy puppy." Lela formed each word with her lips in the shape of blowing soap bubbles. She marveled as each iridescent orb rose into the air and popped with a giggle. *Bubbles giggle now?* She wondered. "Huh."

(Excerpt from Prologue, *Echoes of The Drone Massacre*, novel in progress.)

September 9, 1992, 11:05 P.M.

David G. Kerns

"**M**ax, what are you doing?" Skye asks, switching on the bedside lamp. "And why are you dressed?"

"I was going to leave you a note," he says. "On the evening news they're saying that the storm is turning north, that the winds are up to a hundred miles an hour, and it looks like it's headed for Kauai, headed straight for us. I'm gonna drive down to the all-night Safeway in Kapa`a to stock up on anything I can think of. By the way, they've given the storm a name. They're calling it *Iniki*."

"Do you want me to go with you?" she asks.

"That's okay. No need for both of us to be up all night."

"Really, I don't mind."

"You get some sleep; I'll be back in a few hours." He kisses her softly on the forehead and whispers, *"Kipona aloha."*

The news has been dominated by the devastation wrought by Hurricane Andrew, a Category 5 monster which tore through Florida and Louisiana two weeks earlier—killing sixty-five people, injuring thousands of others and damaging 200,000 houses, a third of which were shredded down to their concrete foundations. In the Everglades, 70,000 acres of trees were destroyed.

The survivors' testimonials, vignettes of terror and loss, filled the newspapers and television—the deafening freight train roar of the storm, the groaning of roofs as they tore away, the screams of family and neighbors, the rising water inside and out, the repetition from one chronicler to the next that they genuinely believed that they were going to die.

The immersive coverage of Andrew's aftermath left little room for news of this second weather system, a storm which formed off the coast of Africa only two days after the birth of Andrew. Until this evening the experts were predicting that it would completely miss the Hawaiian Islands.

⌒

Behind the wheel of their white Jeep Cherokee, Max leaves Hanalei, crosses the one-lane river bridge and heads up the hill toward Princeville, the little coastal town christened a century earlier in honor of Hawaii's Prince Albert. He's surprised at the amount of traffic so late in the evening, and then at the long queue of cars approaching the town's roadside fire station.

Slowing down, he sees what's happening and gets in line. Uniformed men are distributing sandbags and plywood. It takes him nearly an hour to reach the front of the queue. He's given enough for both the house and his shop: six large sand bags and six sheets of wood.

He's tired now and considers turning back, but heads for Kapa`a, thirty minutes ahead. The lines will only be longer in the morning, he's thinking, and maybe the shelves will be bare by then. He lowers all four windows and cranks the tape deck.

The road from Princeville to Kapa`a runs first to the east alternating between rolling pastures and heavily canopied tropical forest, then south along the beaches of the east shore, favorites among the big wave surfers. During the day this two-lane highway, the only route to sizable shopping destinations, to the island's airport and to the resort-laden south shore, can be dense with travelers. Tonight traffic is light, though again not as light as Max expects.

The first signs of town are fresh fruit stands and shave ice concessions boarded up for the night, then increasingly dense single-story structures—motels, a school, a church, a gas station, a few drive-in chain restaurants. Finally on the right, the Kapa`a Safeway, where the parking lot is about a third full. A steady stream of customers, their shopping carts overflowing, file out of the main entrance.

Grabbing an empty cart in the parking lot, he rolls into the store and heads straight for the coffee station and fills a large cardboard cup to the brim. Though he conjured a tentative shopping list during the drive, he decides to peruse every aisle, front to back, hoping not to miss something essential. Assuming that an extended power failure is possible, even likely, his food choices need to be as non-perishable as possible.

Sipping his black coffee as he goes, he chooses two one-gallon plastic containers of water, then a dozen batteries and two large flashlights to add to those at home. His largest haul comes from the canned goods aisle—mainly soups, fruits and vegetables and cans of tuna and chili. He adds two boxes of raisin bran to the pile along with several small cans of evaporated milk. For snacks, it's peanuts, peanut butter, Hershey bars, M&M's, trail mix, granola bars, dried fruits, beef jerky and cookies.

He circles back to the coffee station for a refill, then makes his final choices: cans of diet soda, rolls of toilet paper and paper towels and a Styrofoam cooler big enough for four large bags of ice. At checkout his cart looks like everyone else's, filled to the brim. His requires one hand to push the cart, the other to control the otherwise unsteady cooler threatening to slide off to the linoleum below.

It's past two a.m. when he finishes loading the Cherokee. Pulling out of the parking lot, he's still sipping his coffee, cold by now but doing its job. He's wide awake, more than a bit wired, and satisfied that he made the right choice to not wait until morning.

The drive home is uneventful, the road nearly unoccupied in both directions. Concerned about waking Skye, he leaves the groceries, except for the ice, in the trunk of the Cherokee. As quietly as he can, he puts the ice in the freezer, undresses and slips into bed beside her. She awakens anyway.

"Are you okay?" she asks in a bedroom whisper. "What time is it?"

"It's about three," he whispers back. "I'm fine. It took longer than I thought, but I got a lot done."

He waits several beats for her to respond, but from her breathing, deep and slow and familiar, he realizes she's fallen back asleep. He wonders if she'll even remember his return.

His condition is another matter, wide awake and not in a good way. Lying perfectly still, he feels his heart in his chest and his pulse at his temples. He is physically abuzz and his thoughts are racing—about the storm thirty-six hours away, if that, about the shop, about the protection of the house. Caffeine was a fine idea for automotive safety; now he feels hopelessly sleepless.

He slips out of bed, taking his pillow with him. Stopping at the linen closet, he grabs two lightweight blankets, one to cover the backyard grass, the other to cover himself. He likes sleeping out there, occasionally with Skye, more often alone. He makes himself physically comfortable, but for the first few minutes his mind is still ripping along, obsessing, list-making, worrying.

He'd been a serious meditator, though not for a number of years, but he knows the traditional ways to quiet the mind. He begins with the simplest, the most traditional admonition, and he says it aloud, "Just breathe man, just follow your breath." And he does, and after a few minutes he can feel both his mind and his body slowing down, softening.

Now he can notice why he likes being out there. For one, the quiet—the absence of cars on the road, aircraft above, people talking in their yards, music playing. The quiet amplifies the natural noises, the wind fluttering through the palm trees, the ocean rhythmically colliding with the sand. The house is two long blocks from the beach, but at this time of night the surf sounds like it could be at the edge of the lawn.

And then there's the sky. Flat on his back looking straight up, this is not the sky of his midwestern childhood. On a clear night like this, the Milky Way is bright, an unmissable streak, and the stars are densely packed horizon to horizon. They always remind him of that line from The Eagles song, *...with a billion stars all around.*

Several minutes go by and he, finally, is at the edge of sleep and grateful for it. There is not yet a hint, in the surf or in the sky, of what's coming. Now his mind, rather than being overtaken with anxiety and attempts to control the coming hours, has shifted to the past, navigating memories of life with Skye and his improbable journey in this beautiful place.

His tranquility, though, will be short-lived.

(Excerpt from *Max's Music*, a novel in progress.)

The Writer

Geoffrey K. Leigh

The novel begins to write itself as its author sits at his computer. New ideas and sequential events flow rather effortlessly, including enticing dialogue. He struggled earlier with conversations between his protagonist and a former lover. Creative interactions often required days to figure out where to go next. In this moment, ideas appear just as he finishes a previous scene.

Sergio relaxes as his fingers tap the black keys, forming new scenarios on his screen. The words appear from out of nowhere. He doesn't question it. He continues typing, hoping this emergent inspiration lasts until, at minimum, the completion of this chapter. The source remains an unquestioned mystery, for analysis of anything may remove him from the inspiration.

Was it this morning's strong black coffee? My dream the other night? he wonders to himself.

Stop, his internal voice yells. *Don't even begin. Just keep tapping.*

He does. Then he doesn't. Already, such ridiculous questions begin to distance his creativity. He stares at the keys for inspiration.

Anything. Just type anything.

His novel focus returns.

Antonio, Sergio's protagonist, spots a beautiful young lady in the coffee shop, sitting against the wall at a table for two with an empty chair. He so wants to meet her, to get a name, at least. A full name. And a number? Maybe that's pushing too far for this reticent young man.

The long straight dark hair falls down around her squared off shoulders, now hiding part of her exquisite face as she turns the book's page. She glances up as a man approaches and asks if he can sit there. She tells him no, she is waiting for someone, a friend, he thinks he hears her say.

A friend? A boyfriend? Possibly a girlfriend. Antonio wonders, but he'll wait and see.

Sergio continues to write, wanting to know himself what happens.

The attendant at the bar calls out, "Elena."

The young woman turns over her book and graces herself to the bar. Her full-face smile thanks the barista. She returns to her seat and sips her coffee, then flips her book back over.

Antonio digs deep, searching for strength to stand for a moment, then makes the final decision to walk over to the table and say hello to this fine olive-skinned model sitting alone.

Sergio glances at his watch, as it tickles the left wrist, informing him of the need to leave if he is going to be on time meeting Carlos at the corner coffee shop.

He now regrets having made the appointment. He removes himself from his chair, unfastens and sets down his sacred writing pendant, grabs his notebook, phone and wallet, then exits his apartment.

The street continues its mid-morning quiet, having delivered people to work and not yet busy with shoppers or the lunch crowd. As he approaches, Sergio opens the coffee shop door, allowing an older couple to depart, coffees in hand, before he enters. He scans the room, but no sign of his friend. He spots a young man at an open counter and walks over to order his usual black coffee, grateful he brought his notebook to jot down any new ideas that appear as he waits. The tables are less than half full, and he claims one on the far side of the room, away from the ordering line.

He glances towards the front door as he takes a trial sip of his black beverage, steam rising before his eyes, then scours the room.

His shoulders jerk and straighten his back when he spots a young woman sitting alone at the far side of the room. Her olive skin and long dark hair create an uneasiness and intrigue. The hair falls from behind her ear as she turns a page. A man requests to share her table. She tells him she is saving it for a friend, who will join her. He leaves and she returns to her book.

A barista calls out "Elena" as she puts the cup on the bar.

The young woman turns her book over as she rises, retrieves her cup and sits again at her table, turning back to her read as she takes a sip of the beverage.

Sergio's eyes remain frozen on the woman. He wants to go talk to her, explain what just happened, with an attempt to understand the uncanny similarity to his typed words. But Carlos steps through the door, waves at Sergio, then gets in line to request his own drink.

As his friend sits down, Sergio begins.

"You won't believe what just happened," he says. "I was writing a scene in my novel that just played out when I got here."

"What do you mean?" asks Carlos. "Something happened here that was similar to what you just wrote?"

"No. What I previously wrote happened here just like I had described it. I think I might be psychic, as my grandmother once suggested," responds Sergio. "I think maybe I can predict the future."

"Oh, come on, man. No one really does that."

"Well, how would you explain what just happened?"

"How about coincidence?" laughs Carlos.

"This is too eerie and exact to be just a coincidence."

"Yeah, yeah. I think all this writing is getting to you, *mi amigo*. Maybe you should take it easy for a few days and avoid writing any more."

"I can't quit now. The ideas are flowing too effortlessly. I really like where this story is going. Besides, I promised my agent that I would have a draft to her in two weeks. And I need the money."

Sergio asks Carlos how things are going, refocusing on their customary conversations about life, politics, and Carlos's crazy family.

As Elena stands and moves towards the door, Sergio's heart sinks, missing this opportunity to talk with her.

Carlos continues with his description of his maniacal mother's current illness and constant calls for family assistance. Sergio listens intently as possible, given his intense desire to return to his novel. After a while, he tells his friend he must get to a doctor's appointment, the only excuse he could craft to disengage himself from the current interaction.

Once back at his computer, he realizes how his protagonist can meet Elena. He begins to construct Antonio bumping into this appealing woman at the grocery store.

No, that's too pedestrian. How about a bar? No, a cliche. What would be unusual and interesting?

Sergio begins typing again.

He sends Antonio to the Department of Motor Vehicles to renew his car registration. In the curved line, three people ahead of him, stands Elena. He's certain. She holds papers in her hand, extending out of the same silky green and white blouse, denim jeans, simple blue flats as before, her shiny hair now pulled back into a ponytail, emphasizing her rounded face and ruby lips. Under the papers is the same book she had at the table, *The Catalyst Coalition*, a book he recently finished.

He watches as she moves to the next open window, hands the woman her papers, engages in a brief conversation, takes a slip of paper and moves to the waiting area.

Antonio looks around at potential open windows, attempting to estimate how long until he can get a number and wait. Typically, he abhors loitering. Today, waiting can't occur soon enough. Finally, a woman waves him over, he tells her what he wants, and she gives him a number. He immediately walks over to the only remaining open seat, beside Elena.

As he sits, he turns and asks, "How are you enjoying the book?"

They continue in a brief conversation that includes him seeing her at the coffee shop. Then a computer calls out Elena's number. As she stands, about to leave, he takes the risk of one question.

"Say, could we meet for coffee sometime to talk about the book? I'd like to get your impression of it."

"How about Friday morning at nine? Same place as this morning?"

Antonio's heart speeds up, his breath shallow.

"Sounds great. Thanks. See you then."

Elena goes to the window, takes care of her business and exits the building.

Sergio quits typing. He leans back in his chair and wonders about conducting an experiment. He used the DMV for the meeting place because his own registration page lay at the top of the paper pile on his desk. Now, he decides to test whether this morning's meeting was a coincidence or something else. He picks up the page, grabs his wallet and keys, and locks his apartment, then walks towards his car.

As he drives towards the DMV, he begins to wonder if he has lost his mind.

Why would I even entertain this? I'll feel like an idiot when she's not there. I won't even consider sharing this with

Carlos, especially after ridiculing me this morning!

After he parks and gets to the front door, he stops for a moment, hesitant to enter. He suddenly wants to avoid making a fool of himself, even pondering this chance meeting. Yet, he must know.

He opens the door, steps inside and moves to the line with about five people ahead of him. As he looks around, there is no sign of Elena.

OK, I'm officially crazy. But at least I'll get my registration completed on time.

Sergio stares at the floor, lets out a deep breath, and relaxes his chest.

The man two people ahead of him shifts his weight to the right, revealing a pair of blue flats just ahead, previously hidden behind his large figure. Sergio raises his eyes slowly across the jeans, up to the green and white blouse and long dark hair pulled back into a ponytail, revealing Elena's captivating face.

She moves up to the next open window, gets her number and takes a seat. Sergio looks over to see a man and a woman sitting on each side of her. A small deviation, but close enough for his experiment.

The woman at the window waves him forward, inquires about what he needs, and offers him a numbered ticket. As Sergio grabs it and turns, he notices the woman sitting next to Elena left. He attempts a slow walk as he approaches the chair and sits, his heart pounding even harder. He turns to endeavor speaking with a calm voice.

"How are you enjoying the book?" he asks.

They chat for a moment, he asks about coffee as she stands, and she gives the same response he wrote an hour ago.

Sergio's body morphs from elation to confusion. He stares at the empty chair in front of him. When his number is called, he goes to the appropriate window, completes his registration, and returns to his car for the drive home.

What is going on? Am I making this happen? Creating reality? I truly don't understand this.

Writing becomes impossible the remainder of that day and the next. Sergio perseverates on his chance meeting with Elena at DMV. As he considers their possible interaction the next morning, he becomes abundantly clear he will not share any information about her connection to his latest novel.

Later that afternoon, he decides he will create one final test. He'll write down his sense of the conversation between himself, or rather Antonio, and Elena as they meet for their first planned interaction tomorrow.

How will she respond? What should I create? Or am I simply channeling Elena's life? Is she somehow informing me what to write?

Sergio begins to tap on the keys, describing a candid and decidedly intimate conversation between Elena and Antonio as they engage in their first prearranged discussion.

The interaction excites and gratifies Antonio, generating a desire for more. He asks if they might meet for dinner the next evening. Elena apologizes for being unavailable that night, as she is going to the movies with a girlfriend. She suggests they meet on Sunday.

The light beams through Sergio's bedroom shades early Friday morning. His anticipation of meeting Elena generated restless sleep and early awakening. He arises to shave, shower, then try several sets of clothes before deciding on jeans, a light blue polo shirt, and sockless black loafers.

He arrives at 8:45, wanting to claim the ideal table. There it sits, in the corner, with a man sipping his coffee. No book or paper. Sergio will purchase coffee and hover nearby with no other tables available.

Elena enters right at nine. The man at Sergio's table gets up to leave. Sergio pounces on it. As Elena approaches, he stands and asks what she would like. She describes her preferred latte, just as Sergio had written the previous afternoon. After returning, the two begin a conversation that stimulates similar feelings Antonio had experienced and continues for some time. Finally, Sergio asks about dinner tomorrow evening. Elena explains she can't, but would love to get together on Sunday. She is about to leave when he asks if she has another moment.

"I'm hesitant to share what I've been experiencing. But I can hide it no longer. You may think I'm a complete idiot or crazy. But I need to tell you something."

Sergio explains about his novel and how he described the first scene in the coffee shop almost word for word as it happened that day. He goes on to tell about the DMV inter-action, how the same thing occurred between his writing and their personal interaction. Then he tells her about this morning, even writing what Elena wears without having any clue what her wardrobe contained. Eventually, he runs out of words, a rare occurrence in his life.

Sergio looks into Elena's eyes, holds his breath, and waits for a response.

Elena takes her time before speaking.

"You are not an idiot or crazy. You are coming into your own energetic sophistication, as I thought you would. That's why I have been responsive to your invitations."

Elena again stops, looks deeper into Sergio's eyes for sev-eral moments before she continues.

"This is the reality of co-creation. It happens as people become increasingly sensitive to actualizing their own life while creating a deep connection with another. First, we tune into possibilities, starting with our dreams or altered states of awareness. We move towards anticipation of what most likely will occur with increasing accuracy, connecting to another's choice. It is never a given. But you become increasingly accurate with the co-creation process that involves an aware and active participant."

Sergio gradually brings his lips back together, wrestling with what Elena shared.

"Giving yourself over to writing allows you to see the possible without analyzing or judging the process," Elena continues. "Now, maybe you can do it without having to rely on the creation of fiction."

He puts his hand atop Elena's and allows the air he has been holding to escape. This part he didn't imagine in his story.

"Maybe," he says. "I do want to try."

Faultless

Lenore Hirsch

Sandra Mitchell spent her days trying to help twelve-year-olds solve problems. A middle school counselor for twenty years, she listened to kids, talked with clueless parents, and advised teachers, social workers, and law enforcement. At the end of a typical exhausting day, she had talked down a boy who had called his teacher a bitch, provided a place for a bruised girl to talk about her abusive mother, and refereed the combatants in a fight over cheating in basketball.

Sandra always gave the kids the same advice: Think first and make the right choices. When you screw up, take responsibility. Learn from your mistakes. Common sense perhaps, but not to these kids.

Her best work friend, Marie, often stopped by Sandra's office at the end of the day and this Thursday was no different.

"How's it going?" Marie asked, leaning on the door frame. Sandra smiled and Marie continued, "Want to come over for a glass of wine?"

Marie taught eighth grade history. She was one of those teachers made for middle school. She loved the kids and they loved her. She always had a cadre of students hanging out in her room outside of class time. Although Marie was ten years older than Sandra, their friendship came from a deep affection for the students. And they sometimes rode bikes together. Marie's kids were grown and out on their own. Her husband had a bridge game on Thursday nights, so it was a good time for the two friends to catch up outside the busy school day.

"Sure," Sandra answered. "Let me just check in with Tom and I'll be there by five o'clock, OK?"

Sandra's son, Tom, was finishing his second year at the junior college, hoping to transfer to a four-year school.

Settled in the shade on Marie's deck, Sandra leaned back and sipped her wine.

"So, what's going on with Tom's college applications?" Marie asked.

"He hasn't told me much. I know he's planning to apply to the local university, which would be a money saver. No room and board needed. But he's also interested in the Ivy Leagues. I don't know whether my ex is prepared to foot the bill for that. We'll need to talk, for sure."

"I know what you mean. It was rough getting our two through and tuition goes up every year."

They chatted about school business and then Marie asked, "Did you see the notice about the mandatory meeting next week with an insurance agent?"

Sandra said she had not. Email was low on her list of priorities.

"Yeah, we're all required to hear about some policies available for a good price. Make sure you go."

"Why? What kind of insurance?"

"Well, you know, homeowners, car—I'm sure you have those—but what about life insurance? Do you have that?"

"Well, I'd never thought about it. I'm too young for that. If it's so important, it should be included in our benefits."

"Really? They can't take care of everything. Joe and I have life insurance through his job, but it's important. I'm glad the district found a good deal for school employees."

"Well, first, nothing is going to happen to me. I'm in great health."

"Come on, Sandy, don't be silly. You have a child, a mortgage. What would become of Tom if something happened to you?" Marie was shifting into the motherly tone Sandra heard rarely.

"Well, nothing is going to happen to me. Maybe when I'm older . . ."

Marie set her glass down and leaned forward. "Really?" Marie's face was set in a serious frown. "Sandy, if you don't have life insurance to take care of Tom, you're being irresponsible."

Sandra looked away and waited for Marie to take it back or apologize, but she just sat there. Sandra took a sip of wine. "Let's talk about something else, OK?"

The conversation shifted back to school business. But Sandra felt wounded by her dear friend, and confused that she didn't see things the same way.

Sandra attended the dumb insurance meeting and slipped out as soon as it was over, taking with her the brochure that was passed out. She didn't look at the form and almost chucked it in the trash, but instead shoved it into a desk drawer.

Sandra's middle school was lucky to have a part-time nurse, April. She spent a few days a week monitoring vaccination records, seeing sick kids, and helping when Sandra suspected someone was on drugs or pregnant. April was young and full of positive energy. She had married just before the start of the school year and she and her spouse recently moved into their first home.

Early one Monday morning, when Sandra entered the staff lounge, conversation ceased and everyone looked up at her. Something had happened. Marie was there, her face unsmiling. Someone at another table was weeping. Sandra went straight to Marie.

"What is it?" she asked.

"It's April," said Marie. "Her husband . . . he was out late on some business. His car crashed.

He . . . didn't make it."

Sandra's hands went to her mouth. "Oh my God."

"And," Marie continued, with a quaver in her voice, "April is pregnant."

Sandra sank down into a chair and looked around the room at all the sad faces. How awful for this young, caring person. She couldn't imagine mixing the joy of carrying a first child with the grief of losing a spouse.

Marie squeezed Sandra's arm and continued, "We'll help her get through this."

She thought about April throughout the day. When Sandra was pregnant, she had needed all kinds of support from Tom's dad—physical, emotional, financial. Did April and her husband have life insurance? Before she left for home, she pulled the insurance application out of her desk drawer and put it in her bag.

That night, Tom, who was so often out with friends or at the library, had dinner at home with Sandra. She studied his eager face as he talked about his challenging chemistry class and plans for the coming weekend. His energy and outlook filled her with gratefulness. She was lucky, unlike the parents of so many of the kids she worked with at school.

"Tom," she said, "Where are you on the college applications? Do you have any idea where you want to go?"

"I've been talking to my counselor," he answered. "We're narrowing it down to schools that are really good for science. Maybe Boston. I've got plenty of time until they're due."

"Great, but let's schedule a day to discuss the costs."

"Sure. I'm hoping to find a school that will give me a big scholarship. And Dad said he'd help."

She hesitated and then added, "By the way, I'm going to make financial arrangements for . . . well, you know, some life insurance that would help you out, just in case something should happen to me."

"Like what?" His smile vanished, replaced by a look of surprise. "Are you sick?"

"No, dear, I'm just fine. Going to be around for a long, long time. To see grandchildren someday, I hope!"

Tom grimaced, but Sandra went on. "It's wise for me to have a plan, so you wouldn't get stuck unable to pay the mortgage or your school expenses."

"Gosh, Mom, you're not that old. And there's always Dad."

"I suppose if something happened to me, he'd take care of you. If he's still around." She smiled and touched his arm.

That night Sandra filled out the insurance application. She dropped it in the school mail in the morning, with mixed feelings. *Have I just become an adult for real? Or am I going to die now, today?*

When the official policy arrived in the mail a few weeks later, she created a file for it and showed Tom where to find it. She felt a surge of maturity as she went through the terms with him. *This isn't so bad. He's not going to need this for a long, long time.*

Life went on with the usual ups and downs. Kids cutting school. Parents hysterical over bad grades they hadn't been warned were coming. Tom submitted his college applications, to a couple of places he could commute to and a couple far away.

In March, when the days started warming up, Sandra and Marie planned a bike ride for a Saturday morning. They met at the school, all helmeted up, and started their cruise down gently winding city streets until they were out of town, on a narrow hilly road. Sandra loved the hills, the downhill part at least. She worked hard in her lowest gears on the uphills, but the coast down was pure pleasure, wind cooling her face, and that exciting sensation of speed. If she got going fast enough, she'd get partway up the next hill.

This road was popular with cyclists, even though it always had traffic; it was a major route to the next town. The two women rode single file, Marie in front, and they kept to the right.

Marie crested a hill and was coasting down at a good speed, when Sandra heard a dog barking from the right and saw a big Boxer, loose and angry, running toward Marie. Marie tried to brake and turned to her left, just as a car came upon her. There was a squeal of brakes. The car skidded to the left into the approach of an uphill vehicle. Followed by a crash. It all happened so fast. In the seconds it took for Sandra to get to her friend, Marie had fallen off the bike and was lying in the road moaning in pain. The dog stood a few feet away, still barking its head off. And one of the horns was doing that unbearable honking that means something is very wrong.

The minutes that followed were a muddle to Sandra. She knelt by her friend, holding her hand. Marie's legs and arms looked OK, but she couldn't move her head. Sandra glanced towards the two cars, but could only see that the front ends of both cars were smashed. Someone must have called 9-1-1 because in no time she heard sirens and saw a fire truck and an ambulance. A paramedic told her Marie had broken her collarbone and they readied her for a trip to the hospital. Marie went along in the ambulance.

They kept Marie in the hospital overnight. Sandra went to bed very late. Her half-dreams were full of images of crushed bicycles, crashed cars, and pregnant women.

In the weeks that followed, she spent time with Marie, stopping by her home while she convalesced, calling her on the phone to check in, and using her counseling skills to assure her friend that it wasn't her fault. It wasn't the dog's fault. It wasn't the driver's fault. Things just happen. What's important is to be prepared.

A Memorial for Willa

Brien Crothers

My parents shunned churches. Dad believed religion would tarnish my upbringing. Which is awkward when your best friend is a pastor and it's the day of your wife's funeral. The pews of our community church filled to overflowing, like the anxiety that would have consumed me if not for the person seated one row back. A woman in gray silk, that day's only saving grace.

Perched on a front pew, the widower's place, my eyes cast down the long, carpeted center aisle, standing room only. From doe-eyed children brought by curious parents to men and women in black suits and dark glasses and the many sorts in between, they were people in my wife's colorful life.

Rose's familiar perfume rode upon a cool draft, curving over my shoulders, enveloping me. "Frank, you will get through this." Her whispered words brushed the hairs on the back of my neck, teasing my nerves toward better and worse.

Pastor Zack took to the pulpit. His dark suit hung pressed and pleated, shirt white and crisp, and a perfectly knotted blue paisley tie blazed self-confidence below his neatly trimmed salt and pepper beard.

The murmuring horde stilled. A baby whimpered. From the back of the echo-prone church, an obstinate door complained in a drawn-out whine and died with a leaden thud. A sweater-clad woman with a swishing ponytail slithered into the last pew.

For a lingering moment, Zack studied the congregation. Then he began. "Presiding over memorials is my honor.

Today, we speak of our dearest friend, Willa Michaels, part of this community for over twenty-five years."

Back then, when we first met Zack, we were all just kids. Willa and I were recently married and commuted daily to our jobs in D.C. Not yet a cleric, even then Zack was devout, certain of his beliefs. Our career ladders still lay ahead. He and Willa had their first spirited argument on our tiny porch at that old bungalow on Deer Court. They debated the subject of babies. "I will never birth a child into this world," she'd said from a relaxed posture on a dilapidated settee. The sun had set, and three empty whiskey glasses lay before us as they, thankfully, changed topics to one less contentious. He never again mentioned Willa and me having children. Not once in our decades of friendship.

"Willa's work kept her away for long weeks and months," Zack continued. "She could not talk about her assignments or the destinations of her occupation. She would, though, regale her girlfriends with tales from a weekend layover in Paris or London. And Willa never failed to deliver unique gifts, treasures really, to our Sunday school children."

Zack spoke of the woman I had married. Well, one side of her, the brightest facet, the one that our neighbors saw. Willa loved children, often saying, "It's not their fault they were born into our mess of a society." Those words painted her unwavering worldview.

"Like she was some sort of saint or something." That was Rose. She doesn't always think before speaking.

Zack read from a bible floppy with age and then scanned the throng of mourners. "Now I would invite those who wish to say a word to come forward." A shuffle drew my attention to the rear of the nave. "Please." Zack waved a beckoning hand to a tall, older man in a pristine uniform, its breast plastered with multi-colored military ribbons. The uniform, Air Force. He strode with confidence to the pulpit.

A swell of murmurs filled the church, then fell silent. The officer stood on the dais, not needing a microphone. "My name is Brigadier General Herbert Page, retired. I was a US Air Force Chaplin, last assigned to the Pentagon. Though I cannot tell you fine folks exactly where we were in the world, I met Willa Michaels in a dugout, at a forward base, during a foreign conflict." The general paused as folks, in small cliques, murmured at this revelation.

Finally, confirmation of what I had long suspected. My eyes chose that moment to study the threads of the red-carpet runner.

"Willa was there for one reason," he went on, "for America, for our ideals. Never an adrenaline junky, she kept her head down, gathered intel, and got out of Dodge ASAP. But during those moments between bullets flying and shells dropping, we would talk. More than once, she told me about Frank, her husband," he said with a nod to me, "and of Pastor Zack, a close family friend." He glanced at the pastor, who sat on a vintage Queen Anne chair. "That is the woman I knew and admired."

As he spoke, I recalled a person Willa had spoken of. She had called him "Herb." This was that guy. She never said he was military or where they were in the world. But she told me about a man of genuine conviction. A man she had respected for his compassion and sense of humanity. A gentle man who listened and people listened to.

"My friendship with Willa now means more to me than all these ribbons," the general said as he swept the backs of his long fingers across the colorful awards. "She was a hero to this nation. And my good friend."

With the grace of a much younger man, and not taking the stairs, he vaulted from the platform and returned to his seat.

Again, Rose's perfume—Burberry Brit Sheer I recalled—enveloped me. "And now we should believe she was a hero, too." I turned and glared at her. Her shimmering silk dress crinkled as she sat back and pouted.

Uncle Bob, Willa's only living blood relative, approached the pulpit next and adjusted the microphone to his less than lofty height.

"My sister Jereline had a beautiful baby girl," Bob said with a sniffle. "She named her daughter Willamina, which means the *determined protector*. When Willa got recruited by the CIA, it was no surprise to me."

A collective commotion bounced through the church, reverberating, returning on itself. Though they had their suspicions, few people in our community knew which federal agency Willa had worked for. Many of our neighbors worked for the government in some capacity. Some were with NGOs; others were contractors serving one or the other. The things my wife could not say, the long periods away from home, those secrets gave her a mystique in our community. One that she savored.

"How my sister knew her daughter's destiny, I dunno. Maybe she saw this in her tiny infant's eyes, saw the face of an old soul put here on Earth to save lives and protect our way of life. Whatever it was, and from what we have heard here today, Willamina was *our* hero, *our* protector. She was *my* precious niece." Bob pulled out a hankie and blew his nose.

With Zack's helping hand, Bob hobbled off the dais and returned to his seat across the aisle from me. We shared a tender glance. Zack returned to and readjusted the mic.

"Oh, so she was *born* a saint and a hero?" I turned to look Rose in the eye, gave her a show-some-respect look. I always liked Bob.

"Next?" Zack said as he grinned and cast his hands wide. The crowd returned a collective titter.

A tall Black man in his mid-thirties, wearing a dark blue

suit and black tie, marched to the platform next, stopped on the top stair, and removed his glasses. A band of yellow light cast from an east-facing window, providing him with an impromptu spotlight.

"My name is Danny. As with Chaplain Herb, I cannot say where I met and worked with your friend, your wife," he said as he glanced my way and bowed an inch. "Herb called me after he got the word, said I should come today, say a word or two. I'm more of a doer than a public speaker, but my pappy is a preacher man in the deep south. Off hours, Herb and Willa and I would discuss every issue under the sun. We'd spend our nights at bars in the worst places you can imagine. The chaplain would sip on a single beer the whole of a night through. Willa would pound shots with me. Now, I'm a big fellow," Danny said while flexing both arms, the suit's fabric stretching taut, "but Willa could best me at the drinking game every time."

Willa had told me about drinking with a big soft-hearted fellow, of how he would try his best to keep up with her yet fail. She said he would have taken a bullet for her—if such need occurred.

"You'd a been proud of your lady, Mr. Frank," he said with a gentle smile. "Twice the age of most of us, but still very attractive, there weren't many men who hadn't tried flirting with her, buying her drinks—which she always accepted—or chatting her up. One time, early on, I said I'd pound some guy who was coming on to her. She set me straight right that moment, saying, 'Danny, I got this'."

Calm laughter rippled down the pews like dominoes falling away.

Danny dabbed his eyes, replaced his glasses, and lumbered back to his seat.

I heard Rose move, her dress ruffling again. But she remained silent.

Two distinct drops of sweat rolled down my spine, settling in my shorts, and my sit-bones began to ache from sitting so long on the hardwood pew.

Zack glanced about for the next eulogizer.

A short woman, the one with the ponytail, with wide hips in blue jeans and a beige sweater, came up on the far side, her expression flat, unreadable.

"I too met Willa in one of those far-off places. I never did the bar scene. Maybe I would have if I were as formidable as Willa. In the early days, I'm not sure that she and I were even friends. We had our jobs to do. We did the work, kept to our respective remits. And eventually becoming friends. Through those years, she remained a constant source of support, always ready to listen, offer a shoulder to cry on, or deliver a crass joke to lighten the mood. She was the type of friend who knew me better than I knew myself.

"I will miss her more than words can express, but I take comfort in knowing that her influence will live on through the work she did for our nation. Willa was one of a kind, a friend like no other, and I will cherish the memories we shared forever. Rest in peace, my dear friend."

I looked at Zack inquiringly. He shrugged his shoulders. Neither of us were acquainted with this woman.

She stood for a long moment, seeming to referee an internal argument, then caught my gaze. "One last comment, if I may. Frank, your wife, my good friend, she knew about you and Rose. She'd known for years."

Rose spat a curse.

The woman swayed, her ponytail swishing side to side, like she half expected Zack or me to pounce on her.

Against a heaviness I stood, climbed to the dais, and stepped forward, extending a hand.

She hesitated, but took it. We shook just the once. Then I guided her toward the steps. She walked back the way she'd come, heading for the door, where she stopped. She turned, apparently curious to hear what I had to say.

Zack was at my side. He gave me a quick side bro hug, then backed away.

"Willa was all that. Everything you've heard here today is true. She was a hero, a saint, a good friend. And for the longest time, she was my best friend."

Movement caught my gaze. It was Rose as she eased to the edge of her seat. Our eyes met. I'd never seen such anger in those jade green eyes.

"Willa liked many people. But, for all her goodness, Willa never loved anyone. She loved an ideal."

A chorus of mumbles filled the church. The light in the room faded. I thought I was about to faint. But it was only a dark cloud drifting over our community.

"Willa was in love with her country. To the extreme. But she was incapable of being more than a good friend to anyone. That is how I came to know and fall in love with Rose Michaels."

The congregation's collective gasp eventually fell away, followed by lingering snickers from the back of the church.

"Yes, Rose and I got married after hearing that Willa had been killed."

Another buzz of hushed voices rippled through the church.

"Rose and I were not aware that Willa knew about our relationship." A sea of frozen expressions lay before me. "But it comes as no surprise to me." After those few words, my mind went blank.

Zack stepped forward. "Thank you all for coming today. Willa deserved no less."

He returned to my side. Rose shot from the pews and climbed onto the dais with one step of her long legs, the hem of her dress lifted to her knees.

We, Rose and Zack, on either side of me, watched as the flock, unified by exciting new gossip, clambered from their seats and filed out of the church.

The Piper's Parade

Kymberlie Ingalls

They stared at me with a somber look of pity. Not the kind of sadness, but the kind that said *I'm so sorry I won't be able to kick you around anymore.* Sitting there all lined up in rows, judgment hanging like stale breath in the still air. They had me right where they wanted me; I couldn't walk away.

Marie was the first to approach. She always had the grace and the shyness of a wild fawn. Was her hair really still that Bambi-like color? Not a strand of it was mussed. The freckles were all too genuine, though, even if faded some. She looked real good for a woman of fifty-something. "You always did make me feel like a queen, Jeffy. Not just at the prom, although that night was something, wasn't it? The first time for both you and me. I ignored all of those sordid rumors in the days after, because I knew the truth—that you were just as nervous as me. I let them all think I was your home-base, that you'd been around a few blocks. You loved me then. It was too young to build a life on, but it all turned out just fine. For me, anyway." She tugged at her tailored sleeve. "Just look at you an' me now." Her voice dropped to a whisper. "*Look at you.*"

The next one to stumble over was my no-account brother. Jack never was good for much except being the good time everywhere he went. Mom and Pop had taken him in off the city streets when we were kids, brought him to our little town like he'd blend right in. Cleaned him up and sent him off to school to smarten him up. It hadn't done a lick of good, by the looks of him. "Yo, JefferSON!" His voice boomed through the quiet building. His drunken state wasn't anything new, hanging on him like a cheap suit. "I'm here for you, buddy. I know, sooner would have been better, am I right? But *now* is what matters, man. Now is all we've got. Okay, all *I've* got. I'm going to make you proud, though. I've already been talking to Valerie and the family about the store. Your wife sure has hold of that place, but Mom is working on her. We've got you. You worked hard to keep it going after we lost Pop, but I've got you now. Sorry it took me 25 years to catch on to the grown-up train. I owe you for that." He sounded more mature than I'd ever known him to be, but I knew better. You can take the boy outta Jersey, but you couldn't take the street out of the man.

Oh, and now here was Mom, reaching out for Jack's arm as if she couldn't breathe without him. It'd always been that way, like his shit wasn't brown like the rest of ours. "Sweetheart, they said you did this to yourself, but my boy wouldn't do that. I just know. You were never that kind." Her dramatic cries fell into her prop handkerchief. I had given her one when I was about seven years old. The words "I love U Mom" were inked in felt pen, only the 'love' was a crooked heart. She used to keep it in her purse all the time, but then Jack came along and before they even claimed him as their own, he'd cut another hankie out of an old shirt and glued some lace around the edges. His became a trophy she'd pull out of her bag and show off to all of her friends. It never left her grip on Sundays, clutched in one hand with a worn- out Bible in the other. "Your tie isn't straight, let me fix that for you." She tugged it into place, smoothing the cotton of my blue shirt and brushing invisible lint away with her gnarled fingers. "Oh, I do hope Valerie will come around about the store. I think she will. It's an heirloom, and doesn't rightfully belong to her. Deep down, she's a good girl." Her grimace was quick to turn into a smile.

Mom was the only woman I'd ever seen who could use the steel of her spine to weigh herself down just beneath the water's surface. "You weren't ever a weak boy. What kind of man does such a thing?" Jack led her away.

Brian walked over in a slow gait to look down at me with his square gaze. Nobody else was near. "Hey, buddy." Finally, someone who would be level with me. Silence sat between us, like those nights we'd get high and stare into the blackness of the lake. "What the hell, man? This ain't you." He had the look of a kid who'd tripped in a three-legged race just a'fore the finish line. "This is bullshit. Who'm I going to hang out with? Waitin' on those fish we never caught. It ain't like we had a lot of friends, between us in twenty years." His voice was steady as he looked back at everyone. He was the guy that everyone in town knew but they couldn't tell you a thing about him. "You never could give me a heads up? Didn't I always have your back, you stupid son of a bitch? Listen to me, I sound like a goddamn girl right now. If you were in trouble, Jeff, you shoulda told me." I wanted him to stop right there, but that's not Brian's way. He'd talk for a day and another hour if he thought he could sell something to someone. Some people are born to win, and Brian was that guy. He could go from an alley dog to a tall glass of lemonade faster than a blink."

"Ain't nobody ever knew me like you did that night. A long time in coming, but wasn't either of us going to admit it." He stopped with a sudden look of clarity on his face. "Jesus, Jeff, was this because of me? We never even got to talk about it. I wasn't ever going to bust up your family. I was too much a part of it. Valerie never would have found out from me. It was a thing that happened. It was a thing I wanted to happen for a long time. I admit it. I guess you did too, though." His shame was obvious. "But if I'd known you were going to do such a fool thing... holy hell, man."

Valerie appeared behind him and laid her hand on his forearm. "Brian, give me a moment, could you?" Her voice dripped like warm honey in a cup of tea. Her blue eyes were warmed over, her skin tinged with red as she wiped away a tear. The gold through the window lit up her soft hair. I used to pick dandelions from the backyard because they were the same yellow as her loose curls. I'd put one in her hand, pleading with her to make a thousand wishes. Brian walked away, a broken man carrying a stone of secrets.

There were a million bits and pieces in her eyes when she looked at me now. Betrayal, madness, love. Moods came and went through her like a blizzard of ghosts.

"You and I know what's what, don't we, my love?" Her tone had the crispness of fresh linen on a spring day. I knew that tone. It was often followed with fire. "I'm sorry to have put you here, truly I am. But you were mine, you weren't going to be his. He wasn't going to have us both." Valerie was more calm now, with her face inches away from mine, than the day she'd thrown all of this at me. She never did tell me how she'd found out. Couldn't say if I was more hurt than jealous, even a little bewildered. What a clusterfuck of fucks we three were. Life had thrown us all at each other without ever revealing what we'd done to deserve it.

Now I'm just a dead guy lying in a coffin.

"One bullet to your head, and now your heart is mine forever."

Poetry II

Beauties of Nature

At Harvest Time

Lance Burris

In early fall,
when green leaves
turn red and gold,
and wine grapes
hang in purple clusters
on a sugar high,
ready for their picking
at harvest time.

In early morning,
when in vineyards
dark and cool,
pickers move silently
among the vines,
holding curved knives
in hardened hands
at harvest time.

From the south,
Jalisco and Michoacán
they come,
to stay, if they can,
doing the hard work
locals choose not to do,
sending their children
to the local schools,
in order they need not,
on mornings dark and cool,
move silently

among the vines,
holding curved knives
in hardened hands
at harvest time.

Picnic at Conn Dam

Barbara Toboni

Wind whips lake currents
Napkin plays tag with old man
Hawk sails in circles

Dreaming with Darwin

Nathaniel Robert Winters

I've studied the history and biology
Remember the BC years
Before Colleen
Before Civilization

The lone wolf stalked his prey
So lost deep in the wilderness
Nights cold and empty,
The dark ages.

When the lovely lassie pranced by
The wild wolf was instantly ancient history—
Evolved, canine domestics, like Disney's
Tramp with Lady, sharing a pasta kiss

Years pass, he stakes out a spot to curl up next to the fireplace,
Happy to get scratched behind the ears,
Water and food bowl filled to the brim,
Merrily mated for life.

Envision and Scheme

Geoffrey K. Leigh

Imagine what your world would be like if you heard
flowers blossom, not only on beautiful days, but when
dark with pain, conflict, war.
What if you felt beauty bursting forth regardless of what
occurs, determined to illicit elements of elegance in
every sphere of your life?

Fantasize oaks as they express messages of centurial
wisdom, elucidating how roots dig deeply, allowing a
sway in the breeze without a shift in their stance.
The leaves whisper fantasies and visions of transforming
sunlight into corporeal energetics, verdant green
lusciousness everywhere you settle your glance.

Visualize grapes prospering in vineyards, each varietal
exposing luxurious color and liquid, waiting patiently to
slip into a tank for processing its mature flavor.
Varietals lack competition with other grapes, but rather
aspire to burst fragrant scent, taste that stimulates
savoring, and a lengthy finish to appreciate its gift to
the palate.

Envision the transformation from grape to succulent
nectar, fermenting its best without concern about the
ambrosia of other varietals or vintages,
focused on the best possible nose and palate, enticing
piquancies to enhance the setting, interaction, and
connection occurring with those imbibing the bountiful
bouquet.

Project, as a part of nature, your dream rather than what
you hide and avoid, only recognizing your hidden
masks on other faces.
Unleash the vulnerability to live an authentic life, wasting
no energy to hide, compare, pretend, or energize
illusions that distract from your organic essence.

Conceive the genuine nature of others, seeing through
their masks or avoid attributing your transmutations,
covering the contributions made from another heart.
Are there truly differences to adjudicate, separate, and
determine relative worth when the whole composes all
parts, creating something grander than ingredients?

Hallucinate a world where hearts are wide open, when
people care as much for others as they do for their
persona.
Where people care as much for themselves as they do
others, for sometimes it is steelier to bring the love
inside rather than allowing it to embrace external
beings.

Scheme and endeavor to allow hearts to blossom, express
love within and between, with no barriers to twist
and suffocate the gifts it bears when extending its
energy beyond self, including the source that holds and
nurtures it, sharing undistorted love, vitality, connecting
us with the magnificence that abides all around.

The Sighting

Antonia Allegra

He said there would be wolves.

Not aware we two would break travel codes,
We followed.
Packed bags with autumnal garb,
We flew east to the land of sky-scraping mountains.
Yellowstone.

We chose to pass silent days,
Broken only by sound of wind-washed trees
And the occasional bird call.
      No radio,
             No internet,
                    No sounds but nature.
No touch with other humans or outside voices.

It was our wildlife-fascinated son who beckoned,
With excitement of the news...
Grey wolves had been released.
He was on the hunt for a mere glimpse of the beasts
That now roamed rugged reality.

Our rental car from airport to the Park served us well.
We three met at our appointed log cabin.
By night, we bunked, with hope swirling like the Milky Way.
By light, we shared visuals and studies of our "prey,"
Scouring foothills and towering crags, bare-eyed or binocs.

Finally, on the third evening, we spied
      one
           sleek
                grey
                     wolf
                          on the prowl...

No sighting could have met with such anticipation,
Our search, now fulfilled.

With excited minds, we slumbered deep,
Ready for our returns home the next day...

      Clear skies greeted us at morn.
      We packed and cheered our wolf mascot,
      As we lumbered to our vehicles...
      Son headed east in his royal blue Silverado truck,
      We strapped in our white Toyota rental.
      We shared final goodbyes,
      Still awash in the wolf-found joy.

It was only as we drove toward the airport
That we turned to the radio
For world news.

It was September 11th, 2001.
Two towers were crumbling in Manhattan.

Breaking the law,
We continued driving the rental 'til home in the West,
Across the earth, ripped apart
In more ways than we could dream.

January Rain

Lenore Hirsch

manzanita's wet red twisted trunk
shines like something new
live oak leaves glimmer, free of summer dust
emerald blanket creeps up hillsides
separates dark rows in vineyards
even cracks in the road sprout green

subtle drips and trickles, roar of creek fill the air
hummer wings buzz in search of sweetness
wrens chirp among squawking crows
scent of grape compost wafts over vines

and the vines, the mighty vines:
bare and brown
they cling to guide wires
shunt moisture to the ground
suck energy from mud
and wait

wait for sunshine
wait for buds
to break through
wait for leaves and fruit
wait for spring

The Lone Loon

W. P. Paul

Sun setting on breeze-rippled lake
Light sparkles
Call of lone loon
Echoes

Crunch Time

Peggy Prescott

I grew up in an evergreen world,
Golden Gate Park our playground.
Even our phone number was
Evergreen 6-4248.
In the forever foggy Avenues
I never knew about seasons.

My first Fall at Berkeley
opened so many new worlds,
none more delightful than the crunch
of leaves walking across the campus.
Fall brought football, fraternity parties too—
I was in love with Fall, with it all.

Later there was discovering
Fall vineyards, showing our children
how to play leaf tag, the excitement
of starting a new teaching year.

When then does one begin to see
Fall's obvious metaphor, admit
these October trees are past their prime,
waiting for the inevitable winter?
When does one begin to resist
the year's inexorable pace, want to return
to the many promises of Spring
and the endless delights of Summer?

Still I see a certain lesson here,
one worth heeding. I watch

just how these trees are letting go,
not in quiet submission, surrender,
but with this burst of beauty
defiantly dumping paint cans
of riotous color through their limbs,
enjoying every last minute of their time.

I think of that as I walk along
the River Trail, still loving the crunch,
my new hearing aids over-amplifying
their message—*enjoy this Fall time!*

May, by the River Trinity

Mary Ann Dawson

Three tongues, violet and yellow-veined
Intersect three others,
At which point three more white petals
Curl inward, then fold upon the center.
Three by three by three:
It's a wild iris, a single bloom, lone survivor of last summer's
   patch.
Next to a decaying yet substantial oak stump,
It punctuates its forest surround.
Its white star confirms the good news:
Wildflower season arriving.
My Wilderness.

A cacophony of machine interrupts:
Weed Eater whine signals the annual spring competition:
Nature wild, or nature designed and controlled.
Goodbye, Wilderness.

We urban invaders prefer order,
Paths to the beach free of scratchy weeds,
Gardens with fences; fruit trees in rows; hybrid iris, nursery
   grown.
      Spring... Time for backhoe and Weed Eater,
      Spring... Time to prune and to plow, to clear and
        to burn.
      Spring... Time to save the last wild iris!
Determined, I hoe a ditch around flower and stump,
I widen my ditch, creating a trench, a moat, protection for
   my forest star.

As the Weed Eater nears, I stand on the stump, swinging
　　my hoe,
　　　　Pointing, I plead,
　　　　I shout...
　　　　　　Please.　Please stop!
　　　　　　We must save the Last Wild Iris.

Fig Tree

Mary Ann Dawson

Spied among many of your kind,
You called my name.
Your symmetry imperfect though perfectly balanced,
You were at least as tall as I.

Do you know how dear to me you have become?

Together, thirsty, bedraggled, with spirits at low ebb,
We arrived at this place we now call "home."

Today, months later, I see that your first fruits,
Once tiny and green, have swollen into purple richness.
Blessed to find such a one among fresh new leaves,
A gift sun-warmed and juicy, sweet as honey,
I savor it,
And believe that you, like me,
May survive our circumstance.

Pomegranate of Persuasion

Edgar Calvelo

You hang there from a branch
Blush like an embarrassed child
Caught in a naughty adventure.

Once I mistook you for persimmons
Like when I mistook a pear for a peach
The day before.

You want to persuade me
You are not a regular fruit
Like an apple that I can bite.

Red spherical fruit with a calyx ornament,
Nooks inside separated by ridges
Where dark burgundy seeds hide
Purple caviar wrapped in juicy white pulp
Like a sensuous murmuring praise of life
A bit of sweetness, a bit of tartness delicately enticing.

I can blend your crimson seeds in smoothies
Delight in sprinkling them on salad greens
Or meld with circle of berries:
Black, blue, red, and grapes.

You suggest I learn assiduously
The excitement in breaking apart your hard rind,
Avoid catastrophe of scattering seeds
And unforgiving stain.

You rank high in measures of nutritional qualities
Compared with other fruits and grains
Would you be astonished if the rich ingredients extend
    longevity?

Your stories of abundance and sadness,
The mythical numbers of seven and six hundred thirteen
I would want to hear one day.

You want to persuade me
Not to wear white attire
When I attend to you.
Will you still persuade me
to switch to persimmons?

Rhythm

Peggy Klick

Grains of sand pull tight
against water's curvature
pushing currents, lapping
our bare feet, each toe fluid
indented infant prints;
Tides and ovaries
suck our feet into
Mother Earth's center
rushing foam circles our
ankles, caught then released.

Waves repetition, drums percussion,
indigenous baritone bass
hips unlock, sway to
sun and moon
fire and ice
Aries and Libra
arise, subside
inhale, exhale
shout whispered truths
ebb and flow.

Nectar's Kiss

Joan Osterman

Do you find me sweet?
Do I blush at your bold stare?
Hummingbird, sip me.

A Photograph

Spencer Johnson

The foxes and the fawns wander into the sprawling,
    overgrown cemetery
looking for food, for a place to rest, for shelter
from the cars passing loudly up the hill—
they value the quietude, but don't question it.
What odd stones they are, growing moss like the rest,
but shaped like stumps, some like trees.
The grass grows well, the mice can hide in it, but not for
    long.
Here the sun rises and sets while incessant, verdant life
muses on the dry flowers scattered at her feet.
Here the birds sing in full glory and playful rabbits
bear young on our very beds of ripe decay.
She is too patient to laugh, though, our dear mother.
How sullied philosophy is by intellect grasping at reason,
when all is expressed in every shade
in the grandest flourishes and humblest nods of nature.
What gods we might be in our elevated simplicity!
We are her favored avatar, her very eyes turned in upon
    herself,
but only so far as we go on living by her tastes.

I see the oak and drying grass and feel the day leaving;
there is a lightness in my limbs;
the surrounding forest encroaches heavily upon my
    solitude;
and I feel that perhaps it is part of me,
I part of it, both of us part of something grander,
so that the life of one is the life of all
and the death of one is but a fallen leaf—

a tree loses no vitality in its pruning,
nor even in storms, nor in rot.
What truly odd stones they are—but nature will not laugh
    at itself.
A deer passes quite close, looking—for food? shelter?
I don't know what it wants.
I enter into a poem and become the soil, the trees,
the deer and rabbits and dry grass,
the soft wind too cautious to rustle the leaves;
I close my eyes and love what I become—
open them, the deer has left, and I am a man.
What beauty to see, to yearn, to dream, to acquiesce,
to fall here and there into rhythm with the trees
and learn through much of doing wrong to be,
in such small, infinite moments,
truly and beautifully grateful.

Nonfiction

Almost Peter Pan

Paul Moser

In kindergarten, I made endless crayon drawings of an island. It was always the same island with the same aerial view, mostly dark green, with brown Indian teepees at one end and tiny mermaids in a pale blue lagoon at the other. There was a black sailing ship anchored in a cove.

Each time I finished a drawing, my teacher, a rosy-cheeked young woman who wore her blonde hair in self-conscious, long tresses to cover her large ears, would ask me the name of the island, and each time I would avoid her eyes, give a little shrug and say, "It's just an island." Both of us knew that in fact the island was Neverland, the magical home of Peter Pan and a cast of other remarkable characters, but I would never admit it to my teacher or to anyone else. I was unwilling to expose to criticism the character—and the story—I revered most in the world.

I had been introduced to Peter Pan when my parents took me to see the animated Disney movie in the summer of 1954, and was instantly captivated. The saturated colors of Neverland, the glow of pixie dust, the agility of Peter in flight, his brilliance, his cocky smile and his fearlessness, all served to enchant me. I began imitating some of Peter's vocal mannerisms. I nagged my mother to buy me the movie soundtrack, which I memorized. For the next few Halloweens, I dressed as Peter, complete with little suede boots, green tights and jerkin, and a green felt cap pierced with a red feather. Some days, when I felt the urge, I wore the costume everywhere I went. Though it never got past the planning stages, more than once I thought about getting up onto the roof of the house to see if I could fly.

My sister, two years older, thought I was an idiot. From her prestige position in the second grade, she mocked my Peter Pan obsession, often looking at me coolly and voicing some version of, "You're just making yourself look stupid, you know." I'd stick my tongue out at her, or sometimes even stab her with the little rubber dagger I kept in my belt. I thought she was a snot, with her pigtails, her big-shot second-grade friends, and the white bucks she wore with the houndstooth pleated skirt and white blouse required at St. Agnes School.

In the spring of 1955, my mother held a birthday party for this horrible creature I had to call my sister. Because her birthday was in April, the party had an Easter theme, with lots of glittery pink and yellow Easter Bunny cardboard cutouts and little boxes of jelly beans and chocolate eggs for each of the ten friends who were invited. To me, it was the worst possible display of girly stuff. I wore my Peter Pan outfit that day, a protest against all the frilly, pastel-colored decorations.

In the kitchen, my mother was frazzled, stacking dirty dishes, realizing she had not taken the ice cream out of the freezer to let it soften. "You promised to be a helper," she said, "and not just stand around moping. Why don't you go out and see if anybody would like more Coke or 7-Up?" I slouched my way through the swinging door that led to the dining room.

The girls were seated around the table in their party dresses, happily chattering away. Three girls who had been to the house before and knew me, were the first to exclaim, "Look who's here!" and "Oooh, it's the little brother!" The other girls turned their faces toward me for a moment before looking at my sister in wonderment. "Is *that* your little brother? Honest?"

"Yeah, it is," she said glumly.

One of them, a redhead with galaxies of freckles on her face and enormous front teeth looked at me challengingly. "What are you doin' in that elf outfit?"

"This is *not* an elf outfit," I said. "I'm Peter Pan. So there."

A thin, pale girl with close-set, dark eyes and long curly black hair said, "You look awful small to be Peter Pan." She laughed. "You need to grow up a little first!" The girls all giggled.

"I'm plenty old enough to be Peter Pan," I said. "My mom wants to know if anybody wants more Coke or 7-Up. Do you, or not?"

Ignoring my question, the girls rolled their eyes, snickered, and exchanged glances. My sister said, "Why don't you just go *away*? We don't need anything. You're bothering us." Sitting next to her, a husky girl with short blonde hair and glasses with pink frames piped up in a screechy voice. "You can't be Peter Pan anyway, 'cause I watched Peter Pan on TV a couple weeks ago, and Peter was played by a woman!" Most of the girls nodded, saying "Yeah!" and "I saw that, too!" They were starting to enjoy this game, goading the little brother.

"I know what you're talking about, 'cause we watched it, too, but that's not the real Peter Pan. Some girl with a wire hooked up to her back, up in the air, swinging back and forth over a stage? That's a joke. And Tinker Bell looked like somebody shined a flashlight on a wall. So dumb!"

The girl with the pink glasses sounded bossy now. "We don't have to listen to you talking stupid. We know Peter Pan was a girl, we saw it!" She looked at me with a sneering smile. "Maybe you're a girl, too. Are you?"

She was getting to me. "I told you, I'm Peter Pan, and Peter Pan is a *boy*. And that's that!"

The girls laughed some more, nudging each other. "Peter Pan was a girl! It's true, it's true!" The girl with the pink glasses was triumphant. "So what about *you?*" she said in a sing-song, mocking voice.

I stood for a moment, frozen with rage. Ridiculing Peter Pan was a criminal act. But what to do about it? What would Peter do? In retrospect, I realized it was not the most Peter Pan-like response, but before I could think about it, in one single motion I pulled down my tights and underwear, giving them all full view of my equipment. The rubber dagger slipped from my belt to the floor. I shook my hips for maximum effect. As I wiggled back and forth, I wore an exaggerated expression of horror—bulging eyes, gaping mouth.

The shrieks and whoops of the girls brought my mother running from the kitchen. Just as she pushed through the door, I tugged my tights back up and tried my best to look innocent. It was a lost cause. I saw my sister looking disgusted, rolling her eyes to the ceiling as she said to our mother over the din of the girls' screams, "I can't believe him! What a little creep!"

Even before my mother could gather exactly what had happened, she ordered me to my room. I was happy to comply. I picked up my rubber dagger and made for the door, relieved to escape the fallout of my imitation of Peter Pan's audacity and daring.

At Saint Agnes School the following week, the story didn't take long to reach the rest of the second grade. It spread among the students in the rest of the school only a bit more slowly. It was a sensation, a punch-line that no student could resist passing along to classmates. Eventually even the nuns heard some version of it, though in the telling it had moved into a fantasy/legend category that bore little resemblance to the truth. Some versions had me singing a song from the Disney film—"Think of a wonderful thought, any merry little thought," as I waggled my privates. Others said I was bare-bottomed and hobbled by tights gathered around my knees as my mother chased me around the dining room. One version even insisted I had threatened to pee on the girl with the pink glasses.

Some first graders at St. Agnes were branded early on because of embarrassing incidents in their first month of school, such as the girl who wet her pants on her first day in class, or the boy who vomited on the shoes of the nun who was his first-grade teacher. But because I didn't start first grade at Saint Agnes until that fall, five months after the Peter Pan incident, I managed to best all of these infamous kids by having a reputation even before I arrived at school. I would never be anonymous. I would always be Peter Pan—but maybe not in the way I had hoped.

Where the Heart Is

Kymberlie Ingalls

"Some say dreams are free; I say they're worth what we pay. Dreams? No, girls like me can't afford luxuries such as that."
— a young me

I was 11 years old when I first saw the movie *Flashdance*; 7 years younger than the protagonist, and 40 years ago in the theater. I'd already taken ballet and tap lessons but my awe of 18-year-old Alex and her determination left me wishing I had more than the grace of a young elephant.

Even at a young age, I was a realist.

My loves were song and dance but I was literally tone-deaf and quite rhythmless. Thankfully, my middle-school gym teacher seemed to understand pre-teen awkwardness. Ms. Hanson never required we be a lone spectacle on our modern dance days but rather she kept us safe in groups. At the school dances she chaperoned, Ms. Hanson would smile at her handiwork as we did a clumsy Grapevine, the classic Cabbage Patch or the more skilled Running Man. She'd even line up with us, laughing and dancing to the synthesized beats. So different from my choir teacher who focused only on those who would advance her closer to successful competition. After two years of practicing my scales and feeling stupidly inadequate because I couldn't identify the notes even though I could read them with ease on dittoed sheet music, I was asked with a polite but grim tone to choose another elective.

As I moved into high school I continued to try and find my lane. I tumbled through dance with a stricter teacher, feeling like I wasn't deserving of the black leotard and various neon spandex tights I'd chosen with shyness and hope but I had a part to play, complete with leg warmers and torn sweatshirts. In summer school, I choreographed some friends as we emulated Janet Jackson's latest video.

I kept these things hidden from my family, afraid of ridicule. I asked my dad to take me shopping at Radio Shack for a strobe light and small disco ball because I knew he wouldn't ask questions and I offered no answers. When the holidays came, a group of us went caroling door to door collecting canned goods to donate. Even though I was the boss of the group, I whispered the words in my off-keys, struggling to find my voice. We didn't get too far before our sacks quickly filled with heaviness.

Those were some days.

I've seen *Flashdance* a few times on TV with long gaps in between. I've played the soundtrack a thousand times more. Tonight, I watched it larger than life for just the second time on a big screen and my husband watched it with me, a date night for this anniversary showing. I heard the music again for the first time, the title scrolling across my memories. The taped up toes pounded maniacally on the wood floor with the fury of a young heart. Defiance rang a bell in my heart as Alex determined to dream. Then there was Nick, who followed her home in the rain just to be sure she was safe, I noted the symmetry with my own relationship. Roger also championed my ideas and quests.

I have wondered about that young me who once scribbled about her dreams...or lack thereof. As I grew, it felt that if I put the costumes aside, I'd forget what hope looked like.

I may not live a life of dreams, but it doesn't mean I have not lived. Time, turns and twists have taken me places I'd dare not have gone if I didn't follow what opened before me. I'd not have found my voice if I hadn't spoken out or questioned everything as I do. The closer I edge to the end of my journey, the more I've discovered that hope doesn't need a dream to survive, even to flourish. My baggage is heavy, but there's never been room for regret.

At some point, we need to lighten our loads and let the what-didn't-happens fall away.

I'm no dancer, I said to Roger when we left the theater and he wanted to know if I'd done flashy routines like in the film. He asked did I still remember any tap steps as I clung to my walker, lumbering in the night air.

Shuffle, ball-change, step, heel. Repeat.

It isn't the fluidity of a pirouette that defines how we live, but the grace by which we find our way. It's what we carry forward, not what's left behind. I haven't done a dance routine in decades, but I'll sing along to anything when no one else can hear and it's okay to have that little secret between me and myself. For when I fall and even crawl, I'll carry my 11-year-old heart with me.

A Different Space to Call Home

Stephanie Hawks

Yesterday we were homeowners with a mortgage. Today, November 5th, 2020, there was no mortgage, but no house either. I looked at the raw, red dirt of the excavated house site and the 24-foot house trailer close by. I thought about the entirety of our possessions sitting somewhere on the property, either in 30-foot-long metal shipping containers or just scattered about. I turned and looked out over our 33-acres, barren of the trees that had graced the property before the Valley Fire of 2015. The view made me realize it was not a lot to start a new life with. I remember feeling how permanent, immense, and empty the land felt, wondering how we were going to carve out a place to live and function with no infrastructure in place, while we built our house.

The property in Middletown had been ours since 2005, and we loved driving up there for visits. Now we were both retired, in need of a change, and wanted to pursue our dream of building our own home. We recognized it was not financially sensible to try to hold onto the Napa home over the hard-to-predict span of time it would take to build the new house, so letting go and taking the leap was all part of our decision.

When we left F street in the city of Napa for the last time and drove the 55 miles to our new address in Middletown, my heart was heavy with memories generated over 37 years. We not only said good-bye to the house but also good-bye to hot and cold running water, bathrooms with toilets and showers, a washer and dryer, PG&E, internet access, an oven and refrigerator. Our new living space included one water spigot behind the trailer and an ice chest, the total sum of amenities we started out with that first morning. It was to be off-the-grid camping at its finest.

We had given up a lot to pursue this dream, but we had also left behind asphalt, cement walkways, wall-to-wall houses, people, noise, cars, traffic and morning sun blocked by a school building. We had traded all of the above for sweeping views, dirt roads, no close neighbors, beautiful sunrises and sunsets, birds, animals, mountains, and creeks. The possibilities for growth and creativity were everywhere I looked, and reminded me of why I had wanted to move.

We had no idea at the time what challenges we would face building a house ourselves in the coming months, or what the future held. We would have to improvise a kitchen, a bathroom, a shower. There was no firewood laid in for winter. Yet we were able to set aside all of our anxious questions and concerns. We made lists of priorities, discussed strategies and came up with a plan.

Living here would have its challenges and not be easy, but it was our life to build. A new beginning, a different space to call home. I was happy to be here.

Jay Street

Rick Deragon

The street names suggested flight—Swan, Dove, Lark—and then there was narrow Jay Street into which I flew as a little boy with my family to visit Grandma Alison. Grandma Al's brownstone stood abreast of many others along Jay Street, their wise faces had the patina of city air and harsh seasons. Like eyes, second story windows observed the life of the sidewalks and grand porches, with steps climbing to the first stories high above the street.

Grandma Al and her neighbors came and went. Their doors opened and closed with the rattle of beveled glass, car motors kicked over with a roar and a pop, and drivers pulled away with caution, looking for children, even an errant grandson.

Jay Street pulsated with movement—women in high heels and overcoats carrying home shopping bags, or dark-suited men walking in long strides that made the cuffs of their trousers snap meaningfully above their shoelaces. Stout mothers pushed prams while even stouter mothers of those mothers waddled on wide feet a step behind. Girls skipped rope and the boys played in cellar wells or swung from porch railings like urban monkeys. Jay Street was more an organism of ordered lives than a line on the map of Albany, more a bustling of aspirations and actions than a photograph in an album, more a triumph of my memory than a place passing into time.

In the foyer after hugs and kisses that always left a red heart on my cheek, I faced so many choices. A sweeping staircase with the world's greatest curved banister rose to the upstairs rooms, and there was the main parlor, warm with velvets, curved woods, drapery and brocades, that offered potential drama with slippery floorboards and Chinese rugs—but also hard candy in a cut glass jar that one plucked out ceremoniously, with permission, with silver tongs.

Downstairs had great hiding places so that Iroquois, Redcoats, Black Knights, and even my parents could never find me. Grandma Al always did, though, in the abandoned coal bin where I, like a piece of coal myself, sat listening to the house squeak and the voices of grown-ups filter through the walls. The smell of roast lamb and mashed potatoes made me a hungry piece of coal so I rejoiced when Grandma Al exclaimed, "Here you are—just look at you!"

I would check my memory of the house and note things new and old. I slid down the world's greatest banister and went tumbling across the foyer, landing just short of the glass doors. I raced past my older sister and slid through the parlor, sitting on each chair and sofa, and jumping upstairs skipping whole steps. There, the light became mysterious, so that all escapades were bathed in the silvery glow from a heavily draped window. Everything glistened like Aladdin's treasure cave—glass, wood, and metal were touched by highlights and reflections that contrasted with the ancient shadows everywhere.

At dusk, before dinner, before I had to hide from the enemies of make-believe, I watched the street from an upstairs window. The newsboy shouting on the corner held up the front page like a flag while his other arm clutched a bundle of the evening edition. He paced back and forth, and followed each passerby a few steps, crying out urgently, "Newzzz-pa-a-a-per!" There seemed to be so many of the big black beasts from before the war, all fenders and running boards, but there were a few, like my family's car, that had begun sprouting fins and rocket lights of the new era.

Jay Street still had the cobblestones, the square stones

laid by hearty Dutch and other waves of European immigrants. I imagined the clinking sounds of chisel on granite,
the clunk of shovels, the pounding of sand and hearts.

After being tucked in, I went to the window again to
watch the street go to sleep first. The hollow rumbling of
cars on cobblestone were the only sounds, unless the bell
of a nearby trolley rang as it click-clacked across intersect-
ing streets. Nightfall slowly consumed the solitary man
sitting on the porch across the street, and only I knew he sat
there still, because his cigarette flared brighter orange every
couple of minutes.

The slow music of routine arose and affirmed the magic
of Jay Street. I heard the newsboy, the trolley bell, the slow
clomp of hooves rising from the cobblestones like the most
gentle of clocks. There was the rattle of bottles packed side-
by-side and the tinkling of a tiny bell. Emerging from the
gray-blanketed morning came a large dray pulling the milk
wagon. Full bottles were exchanged for empties as the man
moved purposely to each porch, and the horse stopped on
cue. Somehow, I, who also loved jet airplanes, became a
happy witness to progress, and an accomplice as well.

Grandma Al, proud without pretense, always dressed
smartly—perfect coif, jewelry, gloves—and moved with calm
dignity that deflected attention. In caring for her mother, my
Gramma Lettie, she worked tirelessly, respectfully. She never
talked about duty and obligation. She assembled Yankee
ingredients for the visiting family, creating sensible feasts of
spare elegance, served in silver boats and tureens, porcelain
platters, and flowered China with sterling forks.

With little fanfare, Grandma would go to a closet to pull
out toys: a hobby horse, an Indian canoe, miniature cars, a
stereoscope picturing popular fables. I measured my growth
by noting the shrinking size of these toys. As they broke, she
feigned annoyance, but just momentarily. Sitting tall in her

chair, she slapped her knees with her enticement, "Come here, doll, come to Grandma!"

When the holiday ended, when the magic of this house on Jay Street diminished with the packing of suitcases, I always felt broken. It was time to fly by the signs—Jay, Dove, Lark, Quail—and watch my grandmother's house disappear out the rear window of our car. The newsboy would still call into the evening air, and the milkman would probably ply his route another year.

I, the sentry and observer, brought that mood to the breakfast nook downstairs. Not even sugar-coated cereal raised my spirits. Lost in sorrow, the lost little boy had to leave Jay Street yet again.

I heard the trolley bell when the front doors opened and then I descended the stairs, sliding my hand down that long shiny mahogany rail. Grandma Al crouched down to my level and said, "Come here, doll, give Gramma a kiss goodbye."

Issues

Barbara Toboni

Where did he get that behavior, to slam his hand on the kitchen table? Certainly not from his father. From me, his mother? Most often I just scream and yell when I'm mad. Perhaps I did slam things once or twice, but this time his temper was way out of line.

Family meetings were supposed to be discussions. What now?

Another thing he did was make excuses for his foul moods. It was horrible to see him behave this way in front of company. In front of the girl.

And this girl, didn't she notice? What if she saw he had issues? Back then, I believed she didn't engage because she wasn't a member of the family, even though she was living with us.

Now I was afraid. He was about to lose her. Something needed to be done. But what? What could change him?

I could see this strong-willed girl would take no more. She sat with her arms crossed at the kitchen table. Her eyes glared icily at him. Those brown eyes looked dark black, and they told him everything she was feeling. Even her hair said she'd had enough. No warm flowing waves. It was drawn straight back into a pony tail.

What could I do but be a good mother and keep my mouth shut through the whole business-like meeting? The three of us trying to change the mind of one.

We didn't change his mind. I don't know what went wrong. The numbers were there. The budget was written down on college-ruled paper. He couldn't afford to buy a new car and go to school. How would he ever move out of our house on his salary? He must have known that. But our son stood his ground; insistent, arrogant, know-it-all boy. He didn't want to drive a cheap car. He wanted a new one, and he wanted his dad to help him pay for it.

He looked to the girl as if to say, *Will you help me out here?* The girl—a polite girl—took all of it in and didn't say a thing. Not one word to the inflexible boy. I could understand her position. After all she was young and free to leave. I thought she would go.

Only she didn't leave.

She excused herself from the table and said to him more than to us that she was done arguing because he wasn't going to change his mind. After that I heard the boy's bedroom door shut. The girl could see our son had issues, but she had folded herself up and put herself away. It was like saying *this* wasn't going to be one of them.

Right then, there was a part of me that wanted to fold too, but there the boy sat across from his father arguing point to counter point.

I thought he'd never break his father's will. I was wrong. Maybe it was his father's age. He was tired. His eyes looked weary. I walked away then, because there wasn't a thing I could do. We were a family that learned most lessons the hard way, but who learned this lesson, the boy or the father?

That was the last of our meetings. Our son did move out, but not until after he realized he would have to sell his new car. He bought a dependable used one, but most of the loan burden fell on our shoulders. What was meant to be a generous offer ended up being an expensive failure.

What about me? I wrote this story because I had kept my mouth shut for far too long. I knew enough then not to scream and yell. No, it was the boy's time to slam his hand down.

I had watched the girl, the way their relationship unfolded. She seemed to hold the boy in high regard despite his sudden outburst, and she excused herself from the table at the right time. Perhaps it was hard for her to watch his parents cave in. She let the issue drop, and now I'm letting it go too, much like an awkward-fitting article of clothing left in my closet for far too long. If I share it then someone else may find it like that rare item in a thrift store.

Northern Lights

Richard E. McCallum

A t the end of my summer session at Montana State University in 1974, Bozeman glowed under a rare spectacle: the Northern Lights, also known as the Aurora Borealis. Mimi, a fellow student, joined me in gazing up as the glowing splendors unfolded like a theatrical stage curtain. Radiant blazes presented themselves in a mesmerizing array of rainbow hues.

Our mutual conversation expressed the desire to chase the lights to their source in the high alpine peaks of the Pacific Northwest. Mimi mentioned that she planned on going home to Juneau, Alaska in a couple of weeks, and I asked about the possibility of going with her. The hesitancy in Mimi's reply led to thoughts of while we had been friends for some time now, neither of us had shown any romantic inclinations. Being in a van with me for a week of travel across three thousand miles might be awkward. In addition, the question arose of how to break it to Mimi's parents.

After enjoying the celestial display and joining others at the local college pub our paths parted. Still the thought lingered in my head, and I began thinking about ways I could make it happen.

Then my brother, David, at the time living in South Carolina with my parents, decided to come out to see me. His visit offered a resolution to the potential discomfort of Mimi and me embarking on a long road trip alone together. Additionally, having David along might serve as an acceptable arrangement for her parents.

Mimi expressed her happiness at having us travel together, and Mimi's parents approved of her traveling with a "group" of friends.

Still, I had doubts. I had rent to pay; could I afford to pay for a room I wasn't going to be in for a month? Who would look after my dog? Then the decision imposed itself upon me, and I had no choice but to go. My roommate, who owned the house, told me that he invited his cousin to come out and visit for a month and wanted to let him stay in my room. I agreed to pay the rent in exchange for him taking care of my dog. I was going north to Alaska!

My father gave David a '62 Corvette—an automobile that should have been preserved in a museum due to its classic status. David, without hesitation, climbed into this rocket, which spewed fumes into the driver's cockpit and needed repairs, not to mention new tires, and proceeded to drive it all the way to Bozeman, Montana, where we would meet up with Mimi.

There, the three of us jumped into Mimi's van and headed to Alaska. Dialogue comprised excited descriptions about the natural wonders to be seen and fussing and fuming over the route. Glacier National Park, the first destination, beckoned us with magnificent mountain peaks and glaciers. Biggest concern? Scaling the Going to the Sun road. Would Mimi's old workman's van make it up the grade? Would the road be clear of snow? No way of knowing (no internet or cell phones in those days).

Entering the park, the sign reads: "Going to the Sun Road open." All the way through to the Canadian side. Whoopie! We stopped for a relaxing lunch at Lake McDonald, nestled on the valley floor. The water, clear as glass, revealed a colorful rock bed. As we tilted our heads back and gazed at the towering, glacier-covered peaks above, contrasting against the backdrop of a vivid blue sky and drifting white clouds, we were treated to a truly breathtaking view.

The serpentine Going to the Sun road cut its way up sheer cliffs. Looking down thousands of feet to the deep valley, thrilled and scared us at the same time. We paused at overlooks such as Logan Pass, Hidden Lake, and Jackson Glacier. Each provided panoramic views of a horizon filled with snow-capped mountains. Concerns lingered about Mimi's van as it strained and smoked in low gear to conquer the steep inclines. What would we do if it broke down? Would the trip end? The grandness of being in paradise, the endless breeze blowing through the trees, murmurs of waterfalls, and fresh alpine scents, humbled us and made worries seem petty.

As we crossed the border into Canada, Banff National Park emerged as the next milestone to the goal of witnessing the Northern Lights in the far north country. The sight of Mimi splashing in the crystal-clear turquoise waters of Lake Louise added beauty to beauty. With her Nordic features, blue eyes, and blond hair, she seamlessly blended in with the vibrant colors and shapes reflecting in the intense glow of the water. Standing beside this captivating individual, her beauty and radiating spirit delivered an extra touch of enchantment to the already breathtaking natural landscape.

Heading Northwest towards the next keystone, Prince Rupert Sound, the ride through the rounded hills of British Columbia proved picturesque. Rolls of hay stored for harvesting resembled shredded wheat biscuits. Dark woods framed red barns. Sun rays broke through circular cloud openings, spotlighting white trim. Thunder rumbled, signaling the imminent arrival of the life-giving rain of the Pacific Northwest. Flooded roads complicated progress and uncertainty loomed over ever reaching the Pacific.

Driving day and night, anxieties about the van, gas money, and the need for sufficient sleep resulted in mounting tensions between the three of us. Mimi's irritation with traveling alongside two bickering brothers took a toll on group dynamics. Exhaustion seeped in as the miles stretched on, laboring through endless hours of treacherous construction zones, compounded by relentless rain.

We arrived at Prince Rupert and sheltered overnight in the confines of our van, awaiting the moment for boarding the ferry to Juneau. As we stood in line to purchase tickets, a charming sight caught our attention: a girl with golden locks braided into a ponytail stood shouldering a backpack adorned with an iron frying pan and an assortment of kitchenware. Introducing herself as "Diana," she revealed her daring plan to voyage to Alaska. Accompanied by her loyal companion, Zephyr, the dog, Diana's plan entailed buying a one-way ticket to Juneau and to let it unfold from there.

Diana embraced our quest to surmount a majestic peak in the Northwest and immerse ourselves in the ethereal illuminations of the Aurea Borealis. Her enthusiastic allegiance to our collective endeavor breathed new life into our undertaking, infusing it with a sense of purpose and camaraderie. With Diana's infectious spirit, the tensions simmering between David and me took a backseat, granting Mimi a much-needed respite from the relentless sibling rivalry which threatened to overshadow our comradeliness.

However, my brother, as fate would have it, fell under the spell of Diana's irresistible aura from the very instant their eyes met. Their connection ignited a flame within him, consuming his thoughts and emotions, leaving little room for any distractions. Love bloomed before our eyes, casting a spell on him, and focusing his unwavering attention on the captivating enchantress who had joined our mission.

Travelling up the intercoastal waterway, the scenery unfolded with enthralling allure. Charming fishing villages hosted colorful boats, The communities nestled below white-capped peaks, draped with dark evergreen vegetation and mist-shrouded slopes. Fishing birds followed our ship, anticipating a potential meal. Breaching whales, graceful orcas, and playful seals added to the otherworldly atmosphere.

Finding comfort by settling onto cozy lawn chairs provided on the top solarium deck, we nestled within the warmth of sleeping bags. Weariness transformed into a peaceful slumber. The opportunity to stretch limbs and inhale the invigorating sea air granted a renewed sense of vitality. The deck revealed itself as a sanctuary, inviting exploration and offering the intoxicating aroma of the ocean. It presented transformative therapy, nourishing both body and spirit.

Surprising to me, Juneau revealed itself as a rainforest, where green hues and moistness dominated. Moss adorned the trees. The populated area hugged the shoreline, extending only a few miles. Beyond, the landscape transformed from lush coastal zones to the Mendenhall glacier. Walking on the frozen surface proved both challenging and awe-inspiring. Deep, icy blue chasms allowed us glimpses of the composition below. Along the streaming water flowing from the icefields, David's keen eyes caught sight of vibrant red salmon. Mimi shared with us her knowledge of the remarkable annual Salmon run, where the fish return to their pawing grounds to lay their eggs amongst the pebbles. Their existence culminates after this vital act, succumbing to starvation or becoming prey to bears, eagles, and other predators.

Mimi's parents approved of Mimi going with us, and our party embarked on the next phase of our extraordinary journey. The ferry transported us to Skagway, Alaska, a town steeped in the illustrious tales of the gold rush era. The renowned Chilkoot Pass, a trail brimming with history, beckoned with irresistible magnetism. Accompanied by the dog, determination fueled our hearts as we set foot onto its challenging path.

My brother, Diana, and Zephyr lagged, enjoying each other's company. Mimi surged onward—her spirit aflame with a relentless drive. A symphony of tweets, chirps, and melodies serenaded me throughout my solo hike along the meandering trail demarcated by impenetrable foliage concealing elusive wildlife.

The long and winding pathway aggravated my discomfort caused by oversized and heavy boots, but my disquiet subsided with thoughts about the gold seekers of yore and their struggles. Then the world transformed around me. The once-damp air gave way to an arid atmosphere, and jagged rocks appeared as formidable adversaries on the path ahead. Yet, amidst these challenges, nature's generosity revealed itself, offering alternate routes through the now open vegetation. The wind, blowing through the ridge-lined alpine trees, echoed a mournful cry reminiscent of a wolf howl from Jack London's timeless masterpiece, Call of the Wild.

Arriving at the base of the Golden Stairs, a vertical climb of nine hundred feet, reunited Mimi and me. Together, we ascended the steps, leaving a chocolate bar midway as a sweet surprise for my brother and Diana. Laden with backpacks weighing about thirty pounds each, we paused along the trail, captivated by the historical markers recounting the gold rush era. These commemorations bore witness to the incredible burdens borne by those hearty folks. Passage over the Canadian Border, at the apex of the pass, required a staggering one-thousand pounds of meat per person. Those courageous individuals braved the harsh grip of winter, carving steps and pulling sleds, all in pursuit of their golden dreams.

Reunited with David, and Zephyr at the summit, our jubilation surged, for the scaling of the steps hailed the attainment of our goal. Pitching camp on the flattest terrain available, we gazed at the vast expanse of untamed wilderness. A realization dawned upon our small band—perhaps we were the sole souls gracing these majestic slopes for endless miles. Eager anticipation of the ghostly Aurora Borealis enlivened our revelry, infusing it with vibrant energy. The celestial veil descended, bathing the entire cosmos in a kaleidoscope of hues. Hand in hand, our clan embraced, swirling in a sacred dance evoking ancestral Celtic rites.

I slept in the tent with Mimi and my brother slept in his tent with Diana and the dog. (No one had any romance as the permafrost melted from our body heat and soaked us.)

In the morning, we descended to Lake Bennett, a renowned body of water where the gold rushers-built rafts and embarked on a watery odyssey towards the coveted Dawson Creek gold fields. Nestled beside the lake, log cabin shelters, provided by the Canadian government, beckoned to weary hikers. As dusk descended, the cabin offered a haven in the wilderness.

With the next dawn's arrival, I cast my line into the lake's depths in pursuit of its renowned trout. The first strike caused the line to snap, leaving me with naught but a fleeting glimpse of my huge adversary. Undeterred, I persisted, and the second fish fed us all.

The following day, a hike led us to the railroad depot nestled on the northern side of the lake. At the station, a quaint nine-gauge locomotive billowed steam, reminiscent of the trains built as an alternate means to conquer the daunting pass.

Here, Mimi boarded the train back to Skagway, marking a bittersweet farewell—a moment where paths diverged.

The three of us remaining discussed taking the train to Whitehorse and traveling up to Alaska. The ticket price to Whitehorse Canada included a delicious steaming bowl of moose meat stew, accompanied by baked bread. Delicious. My brother, running low on funds, proposed that he and Diana would hitch a ride on the train the next day. Meanwhile, entrusted with their gear and accompanied by Zephyr, I would take the current train out and wait for them in Whitehorse.

And so, I embarked on the trip alone to the train station in Whitehorse. There I met two adventurous guys from Japan, their hearts set on floating down the mighty Yukon River in a two-man inflatable raft. Despite the language barriers, we agreed I would join them on this audacious expedition.

When David and Diana arrived the next day, I informed them of my plan. To my surprise, David planned to stay in Whitehorse and find work to augment his funds for the trip to Alaska. Diana planned to continue her trip solo.

Our Northern Lights expedition ended there, but many more adventures were to ensue. I floated down the Yukon with the two Japanese guys and survived the Five Finger rapids in their overloaded inflatable. I continued on my own and made it to Homer Spit and Kodiak Island. I met up with Mimi again and returned to Bozeman for the Fall Quarter.

David earned enough money after a few weeks in Whitehorse to resume his journey into Alaska. He met up with Diana at Mount Danali and they spent the winter in an abandoned cabin in Homer, Alaska. There, he befriended a moose, Melvin the Moose, and Melvin slept on their doorway at night.

Mimi finished her degree at MSU and returned home to Juneau.

Diana returned to her home in Michigan and excelled in business and woman's empowerment.

David, Mimi, Diana, and I shared a great adventure and a collection of fantastic memories. We have stayed connected over the years, and on our social media postings we laugh at our youthful foolishness and reminisce about the stunning landscapes. And we still marvel at the spectacle of standing under the Aurora Borealis at the top of the world.

Nola and the Marlboro Man

William Carroll Moore

Berserkeley, 1959

Deciding we needed more freedom and privacy for entertaining our dates, a fraternity brother and I moved out of our Kappa Delta Rho fraternity house on Piedmont Avenue and took an apartment on the north side of the Cal Campus.

At our new residence, we had a friendly landlady who seemed pleased with her current tenant lineup, a group of attractive young people, and decided to throw a party. She invited all residents to what she called the First House Party, suggesting there would be more of the same. She staged the event on the back deck of the small apartment building on a warm Saturday afternoon. Some of the young women arrived in bikinis to bronze themselves in the sun while partying, and of course, to flaunt their beauty. One sunbather, apparently tanning her inner thighs, was splayed out on a chaise as though accepting the sun as her lover.

"You girls look beautiful in your swimsuits," our hostess said. "Please remember though, not to get *too* much sun. Sun-tanning, and especially sunburns, cause skin cancer. Did you know that?"

I had heard this before but paid little attention. The other guests seemed mildly surprised by the idea. There were glances exchanged, but no one commented and the silence became awkward. Probably aware she was sounding like a scold, she recovered the lost momentum by serving us crisp, icy gin and tonics garnished with thick lime slices perched on their rims.

Some of the other tenants were university students, including a married couple on the ground floor. Although some of the women in the building were also college students, most were either already clerical workers or were attending business school to learn clerical skills before taking permanent employment. It seemed clear that most, if not all, of the female non-students chose this location for the college party action and to meet college boys who were supposed to be "Party Animals" and good marriage fodder.

Two of the non-students sharing an apartment had just graduated from the same high school in California's Central Valley. One of them, Nola, was attractive, outgoing, slightly chubby, with bleached white hair and a boy's butch haircut. Her roommate was a retiring, dark-haired, petite young woman who seldom spoke to anyone. They usually hung out together.

I quickly got to know Nola. I talked to her whenever I saw her around the building, and my roommate swapped recipes with her, trading her one for his goulash soup made with beer. She was smart, charming and interesting to talk to—especially for one so fresh out of high school. I learned Nola had been captain of her school women's soccer team, and a member of the debate team. She seemed to be looking for a job but was in no hurry about it. She drove a beautiful 1953 Buick convertible, which she claimed as hers, and not on loan from her car-dealer dad. It was light green with a toothy chrome grill and three portholes in each front fender. She boasted that it had a powerful V-8 engine, and usually drove it with the top down and her quiet roommate beside her. They seemed inseparable, and I assumed they were a gay couple set free after graduation from high school, launching into a new life away from their hometown. Too bad about that, I thought. She's extra cute.

My classes were in buildings scattered from one end of campus to the other, but mostly in the architecture department in the north campus. The Student Union was located centrally near the Campanile bell tower where paths from Faculty Glade and the lower, south campus led to a long stairway to the upper campus, passing through an arched portal in the building. The Student Union, with its bookstore and café, was a favorite place to take a break between classes and chat with friends, or prepare for the next class.

One day as I sat in the Union's outdoor terrace sipping a coffee, smoking a cigarette and reviewing an assignment for my next class, an attractive, friendly young man approached and introduced himself as Luke. With a pleasant smile, he explained that he was the campus marketing representative for Marlboro cigarettes.

"I see you have a pack of Marlboros on the table," he said, "so I'm giving you another pack as a prize in our new marketing program for the company. Congratulations! This free pack is the first in the program. It works like this," he said. "If you smoke Marlboro, leave your pack on the table to receive a free pack from me. If you smoke another brand, switch to Marlboro to receive complimentary packs of cigarettes." His plan was to distribute the free cigarettes to randomly selected tables at different times of day. The goal of his clever gimmick was to have a pack of Marlboros on every table at the Union. He asked me to spread the word.

In those days, almost everyone smoked. We students seldom smoked Lucky Strikes or Camels, but many smoked Pall Malls or Marlboros, the latter becoming more popular after introducing the "crush proof box" in place of the usual soft pack. Initially, I was smoking Benson & Hedges: long, filtered cigarettes advertised as being "For the Man of Distinction." I had paid no attention to the ads until a smartass sorority girl in my French class asked, "*Guillaume,* are you aspiring to be a Man of Distinction?" I advised her that I already was, and suggested she should be more attentive to such things. As a result of her comment, however, I decided to choose a more masculine brand: Marlboro.

Luke's promotion seemed to work well. He distributed the free cigarettes and I was seeing more packs on the tables—like miniature billboards—and received another free one myself. I thought this Marlboro Man, with his "Marlboros on every Table" promotion, was pretty clever; but soon he was at it again, coming up with another program which overlapped with and topped the first one.

He appeared in the Student Union's brick paved courtyard at noon one Wednesday, with a sign on an easel announcing a Marlboro contest. The winner was to receive two cartons of Marlboros and a Zenith clock radio. The sign included a photo of the radio with its beautifully designed green plastic housing sporting a round clock face on one end, a round radio dial at the other, with a louvered opening between for the speaker.

The lucky winner of the radio would be the person who produced the most empty Marlboro packages by the end of the contest. At that time I smoked a pack per day, and thought I might be a contender if I could collect enough empty packs from others. I decided to enter the contest and started asking classmates for their empties. I began filling a 42-gallon plastic bag with them.

As it happened, one of the architecture class assignments was the design of a high-rise office building, complete with a three-dimensional model. One of my classmates had been collecting Marlboro boxes for his model and already had quite a few. The design professor wasn't impressed with his concept, however, and my classmate worked well into that night completely changing his design from one of blocks and right angles to one of arches and curves, eliminating the need for the rectangular cigarette boxes. I asked him for the boxes, but he was reluctant to part with them, thinking he might enter the contest himself. I was so determined to win that I made a deal with him: if we combined our collections and won, we would share the prize. One would win the radio and pay the other half its value. I gave him first choice in the selection, and he agreed.

We both continued collecting boxes up until the deadline. The contest was to end on a Wednesday at 12:30 pm in the same courtyard where it was first announced.

I tried to contact my partner by phone the day before, but couldn't reach him, and he was nowhere to be found in the architecture department. I kept trying to phone him well into that evening with no luck. He had been with his girlfriend in San Francisco, and I finally reached him an hour before the contest deadline. He was in a rush to get to a class and said he would leave his bag of boxes outside his cottage in the Berkeley Hills.

I was running out of time and needed help. Looking out the window, I saw Nola's car parked out back, so I knew she was home. I knocked on her door, explained the situation and asked if she would drive my car to pick up the other empty boxes and then drop me off at the Student Union courtyard since there was no nearby parking. She agreed but wanted to drive her own car. I waited with my bag of boxes in front of our building as her top-down Buick appeared, coming up the driveway.

It was a wild and exciting ride. She drove fast and skillfully. The Buick shot up the steep, winding road to my partner's cottage, making squealing sounds on some of the sharp corners. I complimented her on her remarkable and aggressive driving skills. When we loaded up my classmate's enormous bag of boxes, it took up most of the back seat. Nola sped back down the hill, squatting her Buick to an abrupt halt at the courtyard. It was 12:24. Six minutes to spare.

I swung my bag over my shoulder and dragged my classmate's bigger bag behind me to the podium where the contest action was under way. Luke the Marlboro Man was preparing to award the prize to the apparent winner, one of five contestants, when I dragged my enormous bags to the podium. Luke and the crowd were stunned. The number of Marlboro packs in my two bags was several times that produced by the apparent winner. I won hands-down without a count.

Nola had parked her car and was walking into the courtyard as Luke was handing me the Zenith clock radio and the Marlboros.

"You won! You won!" She cried, hugging me and then, surprisingly, kissing me on my lips.

The clock radio looked even better than its photo, and I swore right on the spot that I would negotiate with my contest partner to keep it.

As we walked back to the Buick with my booty, Nola was uncharacteristically subdued. It was a beautiful, sunny day, and I invited her for lunch at George's Northside Café as a thank-you for her help. She was driving very slowly toward the cafe without her usual chatter, when she pulled over to the curb beneath the overhanging branches of a large tree. She set the handbrake and, turning her smile to me, said, "Wanna make out?"

We didn't make it to George's Northside Café that day.

Frozen Obsession

Antonia Allegra

The 60s were wild years for many youngsters in San Francisco. But in my late teens, in that time and place, the broad world had not yet opened to me. I was a creature who had a strict Victorian, Catholic upbringing and lived a cloistered, protected life at home and in school. Over the years, in the face of controversies that might cause lack of trust, leave it to me to give them the benefit of the doubt and move on. During high school and college, I was deep in my studies, writing, and acting. Who had time to be skeptical or suspicious?

Before I turned 20, I accepted a marriage proposal, not totally unexpected in those days (although my goal had not been to seek a "Mrs." degree). With marriage, followed by working in a quiet library at U. C. Davis, and then having children to care for, my adult life was family- and work-focused. The introverted, reserved personality that had cocooned me in youth and on campus persisted all the way through a divorce, the adoption of full-time work as food editor at the San Diego Tribune, a move to be founder of a cooking school for chefs at Napa Valley's Beringer Vineyards, and then facilitation of the launch of the Culinary Institute of America (CIA) at Greystone.

From the late 80s to almost 2000 when I married again, I lived alone. My house sits in a wood of blue oaks and is a lean redwood structure. Its front door abuts a wall of windows that take in valley views.

During the early 90s, while busy with the CIA culinary school's opening, I travelled to Paris, taking a rare break.

I knew the City of Lights. In addition to living there while my children were young, I was trained in classical French cuisine over the years—at the Cordon Bleu, La Varenne school, at Suzanne Bergeaud's cooking school, and even at Gaston Le Nôtre's specialized pastry school. I feel at home in and near Paris, so this quick trip to visit my friend Joan and to just *be there* brought great joy.

Joan was a freelance writer during my food editor days. She had moved to Paris half a year before, and we planned dinner after my arrival, with our plans to unfold from there.

As I settled into my aisle seat in the coach section, the gentleman seated next to me smiled, saying, "Hi, I'm David Franklin* from Chicago." Being a trusting sort, I returned the introduction, and we shared comfortable conversation as the flight took off. I mentioned the general excitement in the culinary world related to establishing the West Coast campus of the CIA. He seemed interested in food, history, and travel; we chatted about culinary delights that awaited in Paris.

Coincidentally, one of the flight attendants happened to have been a cooking student of mine earlier in my career. After we were well in the clouds, she approached to offer me an upgrade to First Class. Was I interested? No question! So, despite the friendly seatmate with his strong jawline and engaging conversation, I took my bag and moved forward in the plane.

After disembarking at the airport, David found me awaiting my luggage, and our banter picked up again. We talked about how long each of us would be in France. "And where will you stay in Paris?" he asked casually.

Sharing that information seemed harmless. "Hôtel de Notre Dame," I told him before I headed toward a taxi.

Joan and I met and enjoyed a bistro dinner, excitedly catching up on our lives. We agreed she'd return to the hotel for breakfast the next day, and we would dive into the Musée d'Orsay that afternoon. In passing, I mentioned the man from the plane. The next morning over espresso, I received a tap on my shoulder from the hotel staff: "Madame, you have a telephone call." It was David, wondering whether my friend and I might share our afternoon with him. Joan agreed with me; it could be interesting to include him. Our lunch for three was lively and light. We both thought David had been a pleasant, unexpected addition to our outing.

The week continued with David occasionally tagging along. Each time, he added stimulating conversation delivered in his deep voice. The man was well over six feet tall; he moved and spoke deliberately. I felt comfortable with him, and so did Joan. So comfortable that when he invited me on a day trip—by motorcycle—to visit Vaux le Vicomte, an exquisite 17th-century palace outside the city, I surprised myself by accepting. This spontaneous jaunt was uncharacteristic for me, certainly not what I would be doing back in my day-to-day.

Today, when I recount to friends details of that day of exhilaration and beauty at the chateau, many of them are shocked. "What? Toni, you went on a motorcycle with a man you barely knew?" For me, that outing seemed an opportunity, not a risk. Why wouldn't I trust him? It was an unforgettable, thrilling day.

At the end of the week, David told me he wanted to remain in touch. Appreciating his energy and having relished the excitement of my first motorcycle ride, I made it *most* clear that my life at home was full and satisfying, and I had no interest in any ongoing relationship. He accepted my wishes for nothing more than a brief friendship, so when he requested my home address, I gave it to him, expecting a holiday card, at most.

My expectations were wrong. A month following my return to California, trouble began.

David sent letter after letter from Chicago, each insisting on a Bay Area visit to *see me*, which surprised me. His urgent tone was inconsistent with the easy connection we'd had in Europe. I had been clear when we parted: I was consumed by work, plus social and family ties completed my busy life. He wasn't accepting my boundaries. Rather than dignify his requests, I ignored them.

But the letters continued. Exasperated, I finally wrote back, stressing that I would not meet. He didn't care what I said. Rather, his correspondence became increasingly desperate. He demanded a part in my life. To combat my feelings of vulnerability, I crafted and sent a sure-fire letter and thought I'd convinced him to not visit me then, or ever.

Another month passed, and yet another letter arrived. It included a flight number and schedule for his return to my area. "There are items," he wrote, "that I must deliver to you. I chose them just for you." He said he accepted that I would not see him. He swore he'd taxi from the airport, drop off the items, then depart, never to return. I had no say in the issue.

Within a week of David's travel date, I came home from work to find a mountain of boxes by my front door. Their contents presented a curious array: a Swiss cuckoo clock, an elegant down comforter, and tins of specialty teas and coffees from abroad. In a note, David indicated that he intended to build something for my house, something that he would bring on his next trip.

Refined, carefully chosen gifts should pose no threat to me, so why was I so tense? I worried that this man's insistence on a relationship eventually would lead to danger. This was no longer a fun or easy connection. The man was no friend. Clearly, he was a malingerer. A stalker.

I understood then how sheltered I had been as a girl. No longer would I be so accepting of strangers who inserted themselves into my life.

Three Saturdays later, there was a knock at my back door. Expecting to welcome a neighbor, I opened the door to find my stalker. I panicked and shouted, "David! WHY are you here?"

He dodged my question, instead asserting in his deep voice, "I brought something I designed just for you. I told you I was going to do this." He pushed himself past me, through the door, heaving a giant blue duffle bag. I tried to get in his way, but he refused to slow down. He stopped in the living room. There, he produced pieces of black painted wood and a large slab of white Formica. I figured out that he was constructing a coffee table.

As he laid out his materials, I wondered whether I should call the police, or a few neighbors. I concluded that it was better not to provoke this strapping man as he wielded a saw or drill. After he finished the project and packed up the tools, I haltingly told him to leave. In reply, David had the gall to ask to stay the night. He argued that he had come so far and had built this table for me. I reiterated that he had to leave. I called a taxi for him; he begrudgingly departed.

About a month later, Jessica Howe,* an old friend and noted Jamaican culinary historian, was in my area from New York. During our lunchtime conversation on my shady porch, I shared that I felt defenseless against this stalker. I described David and his unannounced visits and unwelcome gifts. I made it clear that I hated that I had no idea what he might do next.

"Ooooh, Toni," she said in her slow, low voice. "I know what you must do! You must use Voodoo to *freeze* him out of your life." Jessica's conversational style intensified. "Do you have a small plastic container with a tight lid?"

"Yes, I do, Jessica," I answered. "Something like an empty film canister, black with a grey lid?"

"Good, good. And do you have a brown paper bag?"

Intrigued, I responded. "Yes. I'll get those things."

My sage friend then instructed, "Tear a small length of that paper and write the full name of this problem man on it." Her voice was dead serious. "Now, roll it up and capture it in the little container. And, most importantly, you must throw it into the back of your freezer, and *never* touch it again!"

I completed the tasks and sat again on the porch. "When will I know that this works, Jessica?"

Jessica leaned toward me and said with emphasis, "When you do not hear from that man, Toni. Then you will know. Voodoo always works."

To this day, on opening my freezer, I see that film canister abandoned in a far corner of the icy chamber.

And David? Frozen out of my life. It worked.

*Pseudonyms

Fear

Geralyn Busnardo

I recently joined a couple of friends in Fort Worth, Texas, for a long weekend and a chance to finally see a favorite comic, Lewis Black's *Off the Rails* show at Bass Performance Hall. In an interview with the Ft. Worth Star Telegram, he identified the theme. "It's basically about a country that has everything any country could ever ask for and can't accomplish anything it sets out to do."

With the crazy number of mass shootings, I found myself feeling uneasy. I was going to Texas, an open carry state where five of the ten deadliest mass shootings in America over the past eight years have happened. Was it the smartest idea to travel to the buckle of the Bible belt, to attend a public event, watch and listen to a comic whose routines escalate into angry rants about politics, religion, and cultural trends? I tucked my fears aside and looked forward to joining very good friends for a fun night out.

We had dinner at a delightful restaurant in the revitalized downtown Sundance Square, so named for the Sundance Kid that hung with Butch Cassidy. Sundance Square back in the day was a hot spot for Western outlaws like Wyatt Earp and Doc Holliday.

We arrived ahead of our reservations. It was prom night, and the Square was filled with teens, all gussied up in their formal wear, posing and shrieking as teenagers will do with excitement for the big night—whatever that meant to them: a rite of passage or the greatest night of their lives or another high school trauma. After all, these kids had grown up under the specter of gun violence. We had *duck and cover*, they had *hide in the closet*.

We took some fun pictures in front of an exceptionally clean, very gigantic silver cowboy hat—total tourist style. I didn't see anyone slinging a gun; I was relaxed, but aware.

After dinner, we waited outside for the doors to open. I found myself tightening up thinking that we were all so happy, and completely vulnerable. No one seemed to be worried about an impending deluge of gunfire. I didn't see anyone with a gun hanging from their waistband and believe me, I was looking.

Once inside I calmed down, and the opening comic managed to joke away my concerns before the intermission. Twenty minutes later, we were back in our seats, waiting for Black to start. And then...

"Proceed immediately and in an orderly manner, do not rush, to the nearest exit" blared out over the PA system.

The hair on the back of my neck stood up and my stomach flipped, a familiar feeling that one gets when roaring downhill on a giant roller coaster. Or when standing next to a client in court waiting for the announcement of the verdict. You know that feeling? A sick but exciting feeling, in the pit of the stomach.

I was ready to get up, to bolt. Were gunmen in the building?

Loud murmurs and shocked gasps started rolling through the crowd. I looked at my friends, who didn't have terror on their faces to the degree I was feeling. I thought I asked if we should leave. Maybe I didn't. It's tough to remember details when fear is coursing through you. We didn't leave.

Not one to miss an opportunity for a laugh, Lewis Black jovially continued on about what a pleasure it had been to spend time with the audience—

A fire alarm began to howl. Is there a particular sounding alarm for gun terrorism?

—and how he looked forward to our next meeting, though he didn't leave at that moment.

"*Proceed immediately and in an orderly manner, do not rush, to the nearest exit*" continued blaring over the PA system.

The siren wailed on, and someone shouted at Black, "Is this a part of the act?"

"You think I can afford this? Good God. Is this real? They're checking to see if it's real." No one was leaving, and I remained on edge. "This is the most fun I've had doing a show."

"*Proceed immediately and in an orderly manner, do not rush, to the nearest exit.*"

Someone came onto the stage and coaxed Black offstage.

I was on my feet at that point, but the audience wasn't going anywhere. The alarm blared. I couldn't spot a single usher in the theatre. Some people had gotten to their feet and the murmuring got louder. "*Proceed immediately and in an orderly manner, do not rush, to the nearest exit.*" Still, we were *not* evacuating, and the feeling of nausea was building inside of me. I was scared. What the fuck was going on?

I expressed concern to my friends. Were gunmen in the building? "Settle down," they said. What? All my life, when a siren wails and you are instructed to evacuate, you get a move on and follow directions. Why weren't we leaving? Settle down? I don't think so.

(*Alarm blares.*) I was in a state where it's a felony to *drive* a woman to an abortion clinic, presumably any-where in the United States. "*Proceed immediately and in an orderly manner, do not rush, to the nearest exit.*" I was in a state where private extremist militia groups such as, This Is Texas Freedom Force, flourish. (*Alarm blares.*) Settle down? I could not.

As I pivoted, more people had gotten to their feet, but still no one looked as frightened as I felt. Finally, and I mean *finally* the ushers entered the auditorium and guided us to safety outside the building. I could not get out of that building fast enough, but there were no terrorists, domestic or otherwise, to be found. No one was brandishing guns or readying themselves for the next great shoot-out at Bass Hall.

After some minutes of standing outside, we were escorted back into the theatre. Some audience members, including the woman sitting in front of me, never even left the Hall. Turns out it was a false alarm, set off by a censor in the men's room. Black resumed his place on stage, the opening comic jumped on stage, stood in front of Black saying, "I didn't realize that my contract required me to protect Lewis's life." It was all a joke, but not for me.

The night stayed with me for a few days. I thought about other frightening moments in my life like the regular occurrence of bomb threats and evacuations when I was in high school. The gunfire in the middle of the night, followed by the drone of a police helicopter and glaring spotlights in my Los Angeles neighborhood during the 1990s. The night in Montenegro when I was taunted in a dark, desolate city park by drunken bullies when Slobodan Milosevic was arrested.

But I never felt terror in the same way I did that night in Bass Hall.

Am I overreacting? People scream at and insult each other on social media, in the streets, in their cars. At least weekly, in the quiet little bedroom community in which I live, a driver glares at me and flips me off with a vengeance. People are angry and getting angrier. On April 13, two days before the show, 16-year-old Ralph Yarl was shot by a homeowner in Kansas City, Missouri, after he accidentally went to the wrong address to pick up his siblings. I deliver food at night and upon learning that, a family member strongly advised me to carry a weapon.

No, I am not overreacting.

Vision at Cobá

Lance Burris

In those days Cobá differed greatly from the more popular archaeological sites at Uxmal and Chichén Itzá, for it was an original—a mysteriously private place in its remoteness and semi-abandonment. Upon approaching its ruins, one shares German explorer Teobert Maler's sense of discovery when he first stumbled upon the site in the closing years of the nineteenth century. At the time of my visit, less than a half-dozen of Cobá's six thousand structures had been reopened to the tropical sun, and those were but a jumble of limestone blocks chiseled by masons dead for more than a millennium.

It was late afternoon when I set out down the jungle path leading to the Great Pyramid of *Nohoch Mul*. The word "jungle" is inadequate to describe the dense mat of vegetation covering the Yucatán peninsula, the thin soil and underlying limestone of which are incapable of supporting a true rain forest. What the growth lacked in height was more than compensated for by an oppressive density which had a damping effect on the chatter of the many colorful birds and small monkeys populating the area. This was no machete wielding trip, for the path was kept open for tourists. However, one had to be wary of the *cuatro narices*, a local variety of pit viper which occasionally slithered unseen across the shaded path.

With dusk approaching, I was glad to reach my destination where the Great Pyramid thrust skyward through a grasping tangle of vines. Its grand staircase offered the only escape from the claustrophobic vegetation of the plain. The climb up its broken limestone steps was not as difficult as I had imagined, and the view from the top was breathtaking, for a carpet of green extended to the horizon, interrupted only by a constellation of small lakes and a diagonal scar marking the road to Cancún. As my eyes adjusted to the changing light, I saw countless protuberances which I suddenly realized were overgrown structures cast in relief by the setting sun. The thought was staggering. The complex was huge!

As is my habit when visiting ancient sites, I momentarily closed my eyes and allowed my mind to slip backwards, freewheeling in time until it stopped on a day in the tenth century A.D. when Cobá was a functioning part of Maya civilization. I opened my eyes, not as a foreigner removed in time, but as a contemporary of the scene below. The day was bright. The sun, being at high noon, flooded the plain with a harsh light which illuminated the smaller pyramids and temples located in the distance. The stucco sides of the pyramids were painted red, black, white, or yellow ochre, each color indicating a cardinal direction easily referenced by the jungle traveler. In the otherwise crystalline air, a low haze betrayed the existence of thatched huts and burnt cornfields visible at the edge of the scrub forest bordering Lake *Maconxoc*. Dugout canoes skated insect-like on the lake's surface, driven before the wind by outstretched butterfly nets. In the surrounding area, limestone *sacbeob*, elevated pedestrian walkways, linked the places of gods and men.

Without prompting, I understood why the Maya had built the pyramids at Cobá and elsewhere in Mexico and Central America, for only from the manmade high ground could they escape the suffocating anonymity of the plain. With fire and human labor, they could impose their will upon the resisting environment, constructing villages for shelter, growing maize for food, and building pedestrian ways for access. However, only from atop the pyramid could the Maya see the face they presented to the gods.

I began my descent of the Great Pyramid using the zigzag-ging technique I had developed when descending the heavily restored pyramid at *Chichén Itzá*. The technique was neces-sitated by the high rise and narrowness of the pyramid's stone steps. Zigzagging provided a more secure footing and a way to avoid the vertigo to which one was susceptible during descent. Thinking of this, I recalled my conversation with the guide at Chichén Itzá, a diminutive Maya woman, barefoot with a small child clinging to her dusty black dress and looking very much as if she had just stepped from the forest. She had that attractive heart-shaped face and bright eyes found among women of her race, and she radiated an intelligence confirmed by her speech, for her words were as carefully arranged as the stones of the reconstructed build-ings of which she spoke. While visiting the site's ball court, she ran her small, square hand over a bas-relief depicting a decapitated player. "This," she said, "is the winning cap-tain," her hand touching the kneeling figure, headless and spurting a decorative fountain of blood. "You see," she explained, "it is a mistake to draw a parallel with the gladi-ators of Rome. My ancestors believed the best must shed their blood for the race to live on. Decapitation was not punishment for failure. It was privilege."

I asked if she had heard that the pyramids at Tenochtitlán, the Aztec capital in the Valley of Mexico, had been designed to ensure sacrificial victims tossed from the top of the pyra-mid tumbled freely to the bottom—tactfully omitting, fully tenderized for the chili pot of ritual cannibalism. She responded by saying she had heard that explanation but preferred another. Whereupon she led me back to the base of the pyramid where she pointed to an array of carved, costumed figures. "Here," she said, "the warriors gathered, led by the great lord wearing the long, green feathers of the sacred quetzal bird. The lord was accompanied by a bound, sacrificial victim who had been taken prisoner during one of many ritualized wars with the neighboring Maya city states."

She went on to describe how the heavily laden procession climbed the pyramid, its members needing to sidestep while ascending the staircase in single file. With each step, the column moved diagonally to the right until it reached the edge of the staircase, whereupon it pivoted ninety degrees to the left. This change in direction was repeated in turn by each follower and reversed upon reaching the opposite edge of the staircase, which resulted in an undulating motion up the face of the pyramid. When viewed from below, the ascent recreated *Kukulkán*, the feathered serpent god, to whom the pyramid was dedicated. Pure theater, I thought. She had to be right, for as I descended the Great Pyramid of *Nohoch Mul* the ritual sprang from the architecture like music played on an ancient instrument. Upon reaching the bottom of the stairs, I glanced back, half-expecting to see the feathered serpent. Instead, I was suddenly aware of a new vision of the significance of the structure, for buried within its pyramidal shape was an enduring sign.

And what was that sign? The pyramid is the architectonic expression of a cone and, as such, a model of perception that is activated by ritual. As the warriors advanced up the grand staircase, their serpentine motion formed a standing sine wave along the line of tangency between the face of the pyramid and its underlying cone of perception. At the top of the stairs, the sacrificial stone cradled the apex of an inverted pyramid in the sky. The two pyramids, one seen and the other unseen, represented the past and future, respectfully, and the procession's ascent the timeline of the Maya world. The bloody act of sacrifice, with the cutting out of the living heart, discarding and dismembering of the body, and subsequent cannibalism, symbolized the abandonment of the self and the casting off and recycling of corporality as the old world made way for the new like a snake shedding its skin. Through human sacrifice, the priests might well be seen as ushering in a new age, the shedding of blood being the price of admission to the inverted pyramid in the sky which the Maya had to descend for its civilization to live on.

Why did the priests not continue the rituals? Perhaps they stopped the bloodletting in response to declining faith and tribute, thereby closing the door to eternity, which brought Maya civilization to its abrupt and mysterious end.

Sailing to Eternity

Stephen Bakalyar

Our genes have only an ephemeral existence within our bodies, yet they can persist, traveling into the future within our descendants. While Homo sapiens sails on to eternity—or however far it gets—my genes won't be along for the voyage as I will have no descendants. Curiosity about the future stems not from concern for progeny, but from regard for my species.

What will life be like? Who will stare back at us as we stand nude before a full-length mirror? Given enough time, one would expect the interplay of genetic mutations and environmental changes to extensively remodel us. However, some anthropologists think that our crossbreeding and high mobility will prevent the fixation of improved evolutionary novelties. OK, but it would be nice if a few things could be tweaked. Like our spines. They have a penchant for lower back pain. As I write this, a heating pad is sandwiched between me and the back of the chair.

Even if sapiens' evolution will be minimal, technologies that we develop might succeed in molding ourselves, our capabilities, and our environment to our liking. Author Diane Ackerman writes that sapiens is a "prodigiously intelligent and meddlesome creature" that is now the dominant force shaping the future of planet Earth. Her writings strike an optimistic note, but I worry about our ability to deal with the unintended consequences of humanity's lifestyle (think global warming and the rise in sea level) and whether our wisdom is adequate to elude the perils of recent advances in artificial intelligence, implantable chips, and gene editing.

These tools have an enticing glitter. For example, when you combine a computer, the internet, a massive database, and machine-learning algorithms, you get a "chatbot." If you request that it write a narrative on the topics discussed here, over which I have labored many days, it will produce a respectable essay in a few seconds. This ability to converse with humans in natural language by voice and writing is an example of what artificial intelligence (AI) can do. Computers that simulate human intelligence processes have been around in rudimentary form since 1956. The world's interest exploded in 2023, when three companies released chatbots.

There is enthusiasm for the future of AI, especially its ability to generate new information and teach itself how to do things. But current systems have disquieting behaviors. Like humans, AI can lie, making up answers that have no basis in truth. It can display "emergent properties," teaching itself skills that were not anticipated. And it is a potential tool for dispensing misinformation by bad actors. The internet could be swamped with text, photos, and videos that are false. The most distressing fear is that AI devices could eventually "jailbreak," taking control of machines and weapons out of our hands.

Geoffrey Hinton, who some call "The Godfather of AI," has made an urgent plea for caution. Other technology leaders have suggested a suspension of development, during which time an attempt would be made to understand the risks that AI poses to humanity. Some futurologists foresee a time when AI surpasses human intelligence and perfects itself at such a fast pace that humans will not be able to understand it or predict its future. Intelligence will have escaped the constraints of biology. Might be a problem.

Unlike the personal computer of my university days—a slide rule that dangled loosely from my belt—implantable chips will be joined firmly to our brains. Attempts will be made to increase our brainpower. However, enhancing human performance will require hacking through a thicket of 100 trillion connections between 80 billion neurons. It's a little complicated.

While we fiddle with our brains, we will be prowling about in the nucleus of our cells. CRISPER, whose developers won a 2020 Nobel Prize, is a technology that can edit genes by finding a specific bit of DNA, then editing that piece of DNA. In theory, it can let us edit any genetic mutation responsible for a disease. If the edits are made to embryos, eggs, or sperm cells, the changes will be inherited by future generations. CRISPER and implantable chips will likely add to the large can of ethical worms that advances in medical science keep bringing to us.

Unwelcome baggage has accompanied many past advances, a salient example being the need to bury nuclear waste that must remain safe for thousands of years. Perhaps technology can avoid this hazard as sapiens gropes for future energy sources. A game changing event on the horizon is the development of commercial power plants with nuclear reactors that use fusion, the reaction that powers the sun. Like current uranium-fueled fission reactors, fusion reactors produce enormous amounts of energy and don't generate global-warming greenhouse gases. But unlike fission reactors, fusion fuel cannot be enriched to make nuclear weapons, and fusion power plants do not produce long-lived radioactive waste nor have the risk of a Fukushima-type nuclear accident. Unfortunately, an adage has long been, "Fusion power is just 30 years away, and always will be."

In the distant future we will encounter problematic events that will be beyond our control. For example, the sun's brightness is constantly increasing. Eventually the high temperature will evaporate the oceans. Driving to LA on

California's beautiful Highway 1 just won't be the same. Might as well take I-5.

We might need to relocate to Mars. However, there are no desirable neighborhoods there. All have low atmospheric pressure. Within a few seconds of venturing outside without a space suit, blood gases would come out of solution. As planetary scientist Pascal Lee stated, "Like popping a can of Coke, you would fizz to death." But even with proper attire, frequent strolls would over many months cause illness from cosmic rays and solar particles.

Maybe we could find a home somewhere else in our Milky Way. But wherever we may be, a cosmic environmental change will come in a few billion years. Andromeda, the closest major galaxy, will arrive. Gravitational interactions between the stars will scramble them, and eventually form a single galaxy. Familiar constellations won't be visible. Someone will have to create astrology 2.0.

My genes won't be around for these events. So what do I care? Well, I do care, out of affection for my species. I worry but find solace in the words of computer scientist Pedro Domingos. "We will co-evolve with our creations. We are Homo technicus as much as Homo sapiens." Meaning, I guess, that we will be able to remain in charge, muddle through, and sail on. The Latin word "sapiens" means wise. We shall see.

Poetry III

Life Experience

Zeena

Kathleen Herrmann

Yemen 2011

Houthis to the north, Al Qaeda to the south
Unarmed protestors fall everyday
We will feel safer in America, Dad says
I sit between my brothers, little sister on Mom's lap, small
   boat for so many
Shoreline blurs, tiny refuge chugs into wide deep strait
16 hours to Djibouti

Chuguh chuguh sputter huff nothing
Captain dashes astern, pulls cord, triceps straining
I'll be back, he bellows, dinghy receding
Dad passes stuffed flatbread, lime juice
Canopus dazzles in twilight sky, dark water slaps hull
Bab-el-Mandeb, we knock at your gate
Bab-el-Mandeb, treacherous strait
Deliver us

Sky blushes
Dad passes green raisins, almonds, red tea
Little sister giggles at my silly faces
Passengers keep watch until sun sinks below waterline
Dad passes dried apricots, fried bread, last drop of red tea
Muffled sobs echo over dark water
Bab-el-Mandeb, we knock at your gate
Bab-el-Mandeb, treacherous strait
Deliver us

Chuguh, chuguh, chuguh
Boat lurches forward, people spring to their feet
I cannot hear my own cries

12 hours to Djibouti
1-1/2 hours to Ethiopia
1,080 hours of paperwork
24 hours to San Francisco
Fast cars, Starbucks
I feel like I'm in a movie
I can't talk to people but I will learn
Life will change for good

Oakland, California, 2023

I can go anywhere, do anything, meet new people
Some return my smile, my greeting, others glare, turn their
    backs
Dark tide rises, pulls me under, tumbles me round
I want to say I'm a nice person
I want to say you cannot know what it means to be here,
    now, with you
But I don't
I hold my breath, wait for life to change for good

Birds on a Wire

Judy Baker

Tiny dots, black on white
symbols, clever collections of feelings and whispers, nested
    between covers
eager to please our eyes
racing along arteries, electrified blood
congregating, spreading, infesting the heart

books gather
perch like birds on a wooden wire
jostling for prime position, politely pecking
clustered for a breath
poised for flight

sometimes words spill from pages
depositing inky truth into the wild
or being shed like loose hair after a cut
onto the floor to be swept up
discarded evidence of life
a collection of thoughts
dissolving into component parts

polysyllabic alphabetical fuel
disrupting governments
rants or whispers
pleas and promises
wrenching wishes twisted tapes
wound tight inside spew broken filaments
shatter glass hearts an emotion-driven drill
piercing fathomless emotion
puncture bedrock beliefs

Poem Set to Brass Fanfare

John Petraglia

What have I done in my life
to merit a musical flourish
like the flashy display
of French horns, brassy trumpets
announcing Radames' victory,
showy entrance in *Aida*?

How do I celebrate
small triumphs of fatherhood
enduring fierce loyalties
a long environmental career
and now, finally
truth poems
I've not sung before
in a fanfare
for being me?

Pretended Symmetry

Edgar Calvelo

Let letter e be,
Wherever, whenever.

Pen extends the text
Spells pretended symmetry.

The shepherd feeds the sheep
The shepherdess tends ewes.

The rebels sweep the cells
Freed serfs weep.

Hens enter the temple
The kettle screeches.

Red, green, slender reeds
The glen, where they dwell.

Bees prefer scented hedges
Deer peek between evergreens.

Between steeples, bells
Between weeds, eggs.

The needle mends hems, edges
The blessed serves the feeble, the meek.

Dew-speckled nettles reflect jeweled net
Pebbled creeks express neglect.

The elegy: Where were they?
The endless empty streets.

When elk meet, ferns tremble.
Elsewhere, the geese veer west.

Gentle egret flees the tempest
Recklessness precedes regrets.

Keen eyes sketch scenes
Revelers render cheery themes.

Seventeen beetles descend the ledge
Trekkers's feet rest.

Seven trees, three nests
Pretzel sets ten bends.

Chef seeks freshness
Peers peel secret.

Chess nerd brews sweet schemes
Tweets terse effervescent verses.

Self sees depth, essence, key elements
Excellence emerges.

They left Bethlehem. They left Egypt.
They needed new settlements.

The desert sheltered the redeemer:
Mystery, reverence, mercy.

The perplexed everywhere remember.
We remember.

California Dreams

Eli Potter

In starlit skies, dreams take flight,
A Moon rock shines, a sight out of sight.
Its cosmic secrets, a treasure untold,
A yearning deep within my lonely soul.

But possession slips through my fingers like sand,
A lunar gem I can't control or command.
Its nature whispers secrets in the breeze,
Bob Dylan's spirit in moments like these.

If that Moon rock were mine to claim,
Life would turn out, no longer the same.
California immigrants, tales bright and bold,
Woven in the fabric of stories untold.

From distant lands, they crossed the tide,
In search of freedom, hopes held wide.
Golden glass shores, a promised land,
Bob Dylan's spirit, they'd understand.

Moon rock, strong, let me hold you tight,
In your ancient dust, a guiding light.
Those who sought a better, mystic way,
In California's arms, they'd stay.

In Bob Dylan's voice, their stories would rise,
Harmonizing with the moonlit skies.
A testament to the human drive,
California dreams that remain alive.

In starlit skies, where dreams ignite,
A Moon rock gleams, elusive sight.
Its mystic allure, a cosmic key,
Unlocks California truths, untold and free.

Frozen in Time

Peggy Prescott

Sunday nights were for *Murder, She Wrote*,
curling up in our wood-paneled family room
promptly at 8:00, no DVR options then.
The cheery music was never foreboding

even when an occasional dead body was shown.
It would not be the bloody, maggoted corpse
of today's shows, just the somehow deceased
whose demise would soon be explained by

Jessica Fletcher, the perpetually perky mystery writer
who moved effortlessly from her Corona
(only a typewriter then) to the crime scene,
usually getting there on her trusty Schwinn.

Her beloved doctor friend Seth inevitably
showed up to support her. Despite their single status,
it was unimaginable they would end up in one of those
steamy scenes that is a must for contemporary crime.

On a lark, we watched an old *Murder, She Wrote*, expecting
to scoff at its dated schmaltz, but instead quickly
succumbed to the welcoming arms of Cabot Cove.
Jessica jauntily bicycled by with a friendly smile,

her only earthly flaw a failure to wear a helmet.
Suspects appeared, not from drug cartels, terrorist tribes,
or xenophobic hate groups, just murderers with a motive
Jessica would uncover in a timely fashion.

The shows always ended on an up note as Jessica
tossed her head back with a chuckle and the camera
froze on her smile. Strangely, when the show ended,
we were smiling too, frozen in another time.

A High Tea of Words

Emily Freiman

Three cheers for triple tiers of
coconut-toasted turns of phrase!
Hats off to havens of heavenly haute.
Carefully chosen words, particularly placed,
waft across a table, laden with scented similes.
Crustless triangles of parslied parley add to
a lightly lavender-layered event,
marmaladed with bittersweet meaning.
Teasy, tangy turnover phrases prompt me to
utter a mincing green scallion of words.
Syllables, succinctly set, salt our conversations.
And his bitter phrases are peppered with minted idioms!
Oh, can you savor the lemon tart of a lingering look?
The nose knows; the mind remembers; the heart laughs.
Cut your acerbic words with an aged, choice cheese!
Lacy and sugary are your drifting confections.
A pungent verbal breeze does please.
Umami mushroom finger foods waft aromatic.
Won't you sample a scone of clotted cream perfection?
Such an idiom piece of lavender cake
that elegantly explodes in the mouth,
leaving a velvety, creamy sensation
of sublime verbal satiety.

Mizzenmast

Justin Godey

I thought about, missed you today.
Wondered when where you went away.
Feels like you just sailed away.
Left me standing stranded on the quay.
Foremast, mainmast, aft-mast.
Downpour, downspout, downcast.
Outspoken, outsourced, outcast.
Misplaced, misled, mizzenmast.
I missed you in the mist as you sailed past.
So vast I missed your mass when it went by on the
    mizzenmast.
First in, passed out, out last, that's a stack jack as you
    climbed up so fast.
Can't get down past, back to the bottom of the mizzenmast.
The one without sin gets the first cast.
The one without sin gets the first cast.
So you went fishing from up on the mizzenmast.
I missed you in the mist, as you sailed past.
Wasn't looking to the top of the mizzenmast.
I don't miss those that sank, or I threw in like anchors to
    the dank cold bottom of the ocean.
Ones that sailed away, those haunt me.
Lost shadows sway, ghost ships, night sea.
Deep in the dark rolling, fading fog of memory.
Ones that were here, but they didn't last, too high to see
    the sea from the mizzenmast.
Too high to see the sea from the mizzenmast.
Life's a voyage, unknown.
Sometimes a crew.
Sometimes alone.

Sometimes a wind and so you ride.
Sometimes in irons, mercy of the tide.
I missed you in the mist as you sailed past.
Wasn't looking to the bottom of the mizzenmast.
Mishaps on the mizzenmast.
Foremast, mainmast, aft-mast.
Downpour, downspout, downcast.
Outspoken, outsourced, outcast.
Misplaced, misled, mizzenmast.
I missed you in the mist on the mizzenmast.
I missed you in the mist on the mizzenmast.
I missed you in the mist on the mizzenmast.

Lean on Me

Eli Potter

Every cold November,
a bus crosses the canal
in Paris glazed with ice.

A shy, reflective November,
a swirling, bright morning,
the eight o'clock haunting.

Lean on me,
I'm the beauty from the snow.
Lean on me,
no boots, no gloves, no coat.

Lean on me,
our life can be a fabulous show.
Lean on me,
we can dream, write and flow.

When winds turn fast and mean,
trust the wheel, lean in,
follow the tracks in the snow.

I'm not a ghost holding a crow,
snow's not melting between my toes.
That's not the riveting show.

Lean on me,
I'm Paris, enthralled in a glow.
Lean on me,
Our future's the dazzling show.

Lean on me,
Inhale accordion ebbs and flows.
Lean on me,
I'll never sit in the back row.

Lean on me,
I'm Paris, the beauty from the snow.
Lean on me,
we'll never sit in the back row.

Dreams

Spencer Johnson

What sanctuary this is that calls me from my unpurged
    senses.
What refuge, my inward dreaming! What haven!
Teeming with intrinsic potential for order,
I grow an Eden from bare soil and people it as I please,
set in motion infinite histories for my amusement.
I perceive in the passing millennia a grandeur of conflict,
perceive the flourishing and decay of many peoples,
of great genius and folly, of religions and ideologies,
of languages and new forms of expression.
All the while my invention is ancient yet virile, unflagging:
the only sin of my art is its wholeness,
by which it is recalled first to metaphors of concreteness,
then to a remembrance, finally the assurance,
of the existence of something called my body
and a world wherein it once in humility roamed.
But what is this? At last, my vision stagnates!
My humility now perceived, such grandeur I cannot sustain.
Dreams fall away into a clear blue morning,
blurs and impressions receding with the night.
A rising sun absolves me in the east, blinding;
and turning, I whisper into the departing west:
Sleep, my soul, even as my eyes awaken;
time will be yours at its end, but now sleep, and dream,
that I may return and speak of what may be spoken.

Contributing Authors

Antonia Allegra (*Opus IV* Poetry Editor) is a coach, actor, poet, and author who writes about food, wine, and travel. She wrote *Napa Valley: The Ultimate Winery Guide* and *Napa Valley Tour Guide*. Toni created three magazines—*Napa Valley Tables*, *Appellation*, and *VINE Napa Valley*—and launched multiple culinary schools.

Yvonne Baginski is a Napa-based writer.

Stephen Bakalyar had a diverse career as a chemist, writing marketing materials, as well as research papers in peer-reviewed scientific journals. Now retired, he writes poetry, essays, and short stories. His work has appeared in *The Redwood Coast Review* and the anthologies of Napa Valley Writers and the Redwood Writers.

Judy Baker's mission is to help nonfiction authors harness their unique voices and translate their stories into impact that changes lives. For over a decade, she has guided authors in unveiling the latent treasures inside their books through innovative, joyful exploration and action. She lives in Sonoma and loves wearing hats.

Lance Burris (*Opus IV* Poetry Reviewer) is a fine arts painter, illustrator, and published author. His focus is on local "place settings" and the relationship between poetry, painting, and prose. He believes the poetic spirit underlies all art forms.

Geralyn Busnardo is an attorney and international rule of law development expert. Originally from Colorado, she has lived and worked in Los Angeles, Afghanistan, the Balkans, Egypt, Iraq, Liberia, Montenegro, Myanmar, and South Sudan. "Working in Compton was not challenging or dangerous enough. So, I moved to a post-conflict country."

Edgar Calvelo (*Opus IV* Poetry Reviewer) is a retired physician. He has taken classes in creative writing at Jackson Community College, Michigan, and Napa Valley College. He enjoys playing chess, tries to walk the river every day and stops along the way to read. He lives in Napa with his wife.

Brien Crothers (*Opus IV* Fiction Reviewer) loves travel and writing, particularly YA adventures and slice-of-life short stories. His latest self-published work is *Camino Child*, a novel set on the Camino de Santiago in Spain. He has also written for *UltraRunning Magazine* and had a story about a pink church published in the Napa Valley Writers 2021 anthology.

Mary Ann Dawson after moving to Eureka, CA, in 1962, earned an MA in the Teaching of Writing, and taught English. She also became a fellow of the Redwood Writing Project. After moving to Napa in 2013, Dawson learned about Napa Valley Writers from two friends/NVW members and, inspired by poet laureate Marianne Lyon, she began to write poetry.

Rick Deragon earned BA/MAs in Art/Art History at CSU Chico. He lived in Paris and taught at Notre Dame de Namur University. He was curator at the Monterey Museum of Art, art critic for the *Monterey Herald*, and director at the Napa Valley Museum. He published *Fire in the Year of Four Emperors* in 2017. He is married with one son.

Bruce Fleming (Cover Photographer) is a native Californian and artist. He secured his first commercial art job at the age of twelve. Along the way, he's worked as an illustrator, designer, craftsman, executive chef, photographer, and inventor. For 30 years, Bruce has been traveling the globe, photographing for advertiser, travel, food & lifestyle publications.

Emily Freiman has written poetry, stories, and songs since childhood. She is a 45-year resident of northern California, artist, writer, instructor, and past board member. Her course and her forthcoming facilitator workbook, *Invite the Muse*, utilize writing, poetry, and artmaking in community as creativity modalities. Two of her poems are published in Napa Valley Writers *Third Harvest* Anthology.

Justin Godey is an independent author living in Napa Valley. When Godey's first child was born, he left his job as a computer programmer to become a stay-at-home dad. Raising two kids brought him in closer touch with his creative side. Now he is pursuing a career as an independent author, poet, and songwriter.

Stephanie Hawks is a retired music teacher with the Napa Valley Unified School District. She spends her time working with her husband, family, and friends, building her house up in Middletown. Besides acquiring carpentry skills and being an equipment operator, she also enjoys playing viola with the Lake County Symphony.

Kathleen Herrmann is called by life's unexpected happenings, expressing personal discovery in poetry and song. She has published her work in numerous anthologies and is currently writing a poetry book entitled *I Was There, Now I'm Here: Refugees in America*.

Lenore Hirsch (Opus IV Fiction Section Editor) is a retired educator. She writes fiction, poetry, memoir, and humor. Her books include *My Leash on Life: Foxy's View of the World from a Foot Off the Ground*; a poetry collection, *Leavings*; *Laugh and Live: Advice for Aging Boomers*; and *Schooled: Confessions of a Rookie Vice Principal*.

Kymberlie Ingalls is an award-winning essayist, writing coach and speaker. She is the author of blog sites *Writer of the Storm* and *Neuroticy = A Societal Madness*, short fiction and the books *43*, and *Bridges; A Lifetime In Essay*. Her work focuses on love, grief, and aging with examination of humanity and the heart. Beware of falling opinions.

Spencer Johnson A native of Oregon, Spencer lives in the Napa Valley with his wife and three boys. His poetry and fiction explore, among other themes, the human soul as a piece of nature and human life and art as a strange, beautiful outgrowth of this nature.

David G. Kerns is a Napa-based novelist and journalist. Following a career as a physician and Stanford medical professor, he produced two published novels and has been freelance writing for the *Napa Valley Register* since 2011. His current book-in-progress, a work of historical fiction, is set in Kaua'i.

Jeffrey Kingman's poetry collection, *Beyond that Hill I Gather*, was published by Finishing Line Press in June 2021. He is the winner of the 2018 Eyelands Book Award for an unpublished poetry book, and a finalist in the 2018 Hillary Gravendyk Prize book competition.

Peggy Klick has practiced meditation and creative writing with Albert Flynn DeSilver of Marin. Peggy is a founding member of the international writing community Mindful Authors Accelerated. Her poetry is published in *Writing into Truth* and *Emerging into Light*. She is writing a novel and lives in the Napa Valley.

Geoffrey K. Leigh (*Opus IV* Fiction Reviewer) taught and conducted social science research in academia for 30 years, writing publications and co-editing *Adolescence in Families*. In Napa Valley since 2009, he works at a winery. He has published the non-fiction *Rekindling Our Cosmic Spark* (2017), fiction *Dancing with Audacity* (2021) and a combination of fiction and poetry, *Prosetry Journey* (2023) with Marianne Lyon.

Marianne Lyon (*Opus IV* Poetry Reviewer) taught music for 43 years, including in Hong Kong and Nicaragua. She has been published in literary magazines and reviews and was nominated for the 2016 Pushcart Award. A member of California Writers Club, Napa Valley Writers, and Solstice Writers, she is Adjunct Professor at Touro University. She was Napa County's Poet Laureate 2021–2023.

Richard E. McCallum obtained a BS in Film/TV from Montana State (1976) and MA from USC (1983 – Cinema). Richard served in the Navy as a combat camera operator. He worked in the film/multimedia industry in Los Angeles and San Francisco. Richard is a member of the San Francisco Peninsula, Napa Valley, and High Desert branches of the California Writers Club.

William Carroll Moore lives in Napa Valley and writes fiction and non-fiction. After earning a BS in architecture at UC, Berkeley and an MS in urban planning at Athens Technological Institute in Greece, his professional career included technical writing and teaching at California Polytechnic State University in San Luis Obispo.

Paul Moser (*Opus IV* Non-Fiction Reviewer) is the author of four books, three of them reflecting a flagrant, indefensible obsession with satire and parody: *The New Revised Catechlysm*, *T-Bull and the Lost Men*, and *Inside the Flavor League*. The fourth is a memoir titled *Seeking*.

Carole Malone Nelson has lived in the Bay Area since she started at Cal, except for the 12 years she and her husband, Gene, lived on Kaua'i following their retirement. She has published a memoir about those 12 years titled *Well Now You've Done It!* and another about their extensive travel titled *What in the World Are You Doing Here?*

Joan Osterman lives in Napa, where she explores the magic in everyday life through poetry, memoir, and fiction. Her work has been published in the California Writers Club 2022 *Literary Review* and several Napa Valley Writers anthologies. She presents her poetry at venues throughout the Bay Area.

W. P. Paul is one of billions of human siblings who dream of a period of sustainability and inclusivity enlightenment. W. P. Paul writes in poetry and science fiction genres.

John Petraglia (*Opus IV* Managing Editor) is a Napa poet, writer/editor, and former environmental communications professional. He is a Board Member of Napa Valley Writers, was Poetry Editor of the Napa Valley Writers anthology, *Third Harvest*, and Managing Editor of Napa Valley Writers 2023 anthology, *Opus IV*.

Eli Potter is an investor, advising startups on technology at scale. In the past, she served as an executive at Coinbase and Autodesk, fundamentally changing the product engineering culture. Eli holds an MS degree from Carnegie Mellon University, writes fiction, and donates a tech scholarship to the San Francisco Writers Conference.

Peggy Prescott (*Opus IV* Non-Fiction Reviewer) retired from elementary school teaching and began taking classes with George Stratton. During that time, she won multiple Jessamyn West Awards in fiction, non-fiction, and poetry. She works regularly with the local Solstice Writers. Her book *Neurotic's Guide to Retirement* was published in 2010.

Brad Shurmantine lives in Napa where he writes, reads, and tends three gardens. His fiction and essays have appeared in *Monday Night*, *Flint Hills Review*, and *Catamaran*; his poetry in *Third Wednesday*, *Cacti Fur*, and *Blue Lake Review*. He backpacks, travels, and prefers George Eliot to Charles Dickens. See bradshurmantine.com.

Barbara Toboni has published three poetry collections: *Undertow*, *Water Over Time*, and *Light the Way*; and two children's books: *The Bunny Poets* and *The Bunny Poets and the Library Book*. Her work appears in anthologies and online. She is a mother and grandmother and lives in the Napa Valley with her husband. See barbaratoboni.com.

Nathaniel Robert "Bob" Winters joined the Navy from New York City. The Vietnam veteran earned his BA from Sonoma State College and an MA degree from California State University, Stanislaus. He has written a variety of books. Bob lives with his wife in Napa Valley. Despite having Parkinson's disease, he writes almost every day.

Sponsor Acknowledgement

Napa Valley Writers thanks the following Community and Individual Sponsors for their generous support of our mission and publication of *Opus IV 2023 Napa Valley Writers Anthology.*

Community Sponsors

Antonia (Toni) Allegra

Writing Coach • Writer • Culinary Professional
P.O. Box 663, St. Helena, CA 94574

Napa Bookmine • Naomi Chamblin

We sell new and used books to the Napa community, now with a full coffee bar in our new location. Find us at 4 places: 1625 2nd Street (Napa), inside Oxbow Public Market (Napa); 1315 Main Street, St. Helena. You can buy books from us 24/7 at napabookmine.com

Lance Burris

Writer • Painter • Poet

Cornerstone Cellars

Cornerstone started with a conversation between friends over a glass of wine. Three decades later, we make wines with classic varietal attributes that are approachable and delicious. We combine Napa Valley ease with a welcoming Southern approach to entertaining. We love what we do. Come find out for yourself. Cornerstonecellars.com

Community Sponsors

Rianda House

We increase life expectations by providing programs and activities to keep older adults strong in mind, body, and spirit, connected in meaningful relationships, and giving from the abundance of their lives.
1475 Main St, St. Helena, CA (707) 963-8555

The White Barn

2727 Sulphur Springs Av., St. Helena, CA 94574
www.thewhitebarn.org • Tel. 707-987-8225

Individual Sponsors

Brien Crothers
Emily Freiman
David G. Kerns
Claudia Hagadus Long
Marianne Lyon
Marty Malin
Joan Osterman
Jessica Vapnek

About Napa Valley Writers

Napa Valley Writers was founded in 2012 when a group of writers with a variety of interests and genres met at the Napa library to explore the possibility of chartering a new chapter of the California Writers Club. The California Writers Club was founded in 1909 and is one of the oldest literary clubs in the United States.

Napa Valley Writers fosters professionalism in writing, promotes networking of writers within the Napa Valley writing community and beyond, mentors new and experienced writers of all ages, and provides literary support for writers and the writing community. We support all genres including poetry, fiction and non-fiction and their subgenres, as well as all writing styles and related literary professions such as editing, publishing, and journalism.

Napa Valley Writers provides an environment where members can share their work, obtain critiques of their efforts, and attend informational and improvement-oriented workshops. Our writers share their experiences and their writing with the wider community through readings and salons, and our biannual Anthology (2017, 2019, 2021, 2023). We promote an appreciation of literature and the art of writing through outreach and educational programs for adults and youth.

Napa Valley Writers meets on the second Wednesday night of every month from 7 to 9 p.m. Our meeting format includes a poetry invocation and time for networking, announcements of classes and contests and member writing successes, a short reading by a member, and an invited speaker and Q&A on the writing craft, challenges, and success of writing and ancillary fields.

See our website (http://napavalleywriters.org) for up-to-date information about meeting locations and for membership information.

Want to join Napa Valley Writers? Have any questions? Visit our Facebook page at: www.facebook.com/nvwritersclub. or contact us at: napavalleywriters@gmail.com.